Science 9
Concepts and Connections

D1468528

NELSON

Science 9
Concepts and Connections

Student Record of Learning

Program Consultants

Ted Gibb
Formerly of Thames Valley District School Board

Barry LeDrew
Formerly of Newfoundland Department of Education

Authors

Ted Gibb
Formerly of Thames Valley District School Board

Barry LeDrew
Formerly of Newfoundland Department of Education

Donna Osborne
Ottawa-Carleton District School Board

John Patterson
Algoma District School Board

Jill Roberts
Formerly of Ottawa-Carleton District School Board

Meredith White-McMahon
St. James-Assiniboia School Division

THOMSON

NELSON

Australia • Canada • Mexico • Singapore • Spain • United Kingdom • United States

THOMSON

NELSON

Nelson Science 9
Concepts and Connections
Student Record of Learning

Program Consultants
Ted Gibb
Barry LeDrew

Authors
Ted Gibb
Barry LeDrew
Donna Osborne
John Patterson
Jill Roberts
Meredith White-McMahon

Director of Publishing
David Steele

Publisher
Kevin Martindale

Program Manager
Tony Rodrigues

Developmental Editor
Lee Geller

Editorial Assistant
Matthew Roberts

Senior Managing Editor
Nicola Balfour

Senior Production Editor
Joanne Close

Copy Editors
Claudia Kutchukian
Dawn Hunter

Production Coordinator
Julie Preston

Creative Director
Angela Cluer

Art Management
Suzanne Peden

Composition
Computer Composition of Canada

Illustrators
Andrew Breithaupt
Steven Corrigan
Deborah Crowle
Frank Netter
Myra Rudakewich
Bart Vallecoccia
Jane Whitney

Cover Design
Peter Papayanakis

Cover Image
NASA/Science Photo Library

Printer
Webcom

National Library of Canada Cataloguing in Publication Data

Main entry under title:
Gibb, Ted
   Science 9: concepts and connections. Student record of learning/Ted Gibb, Barry LeDrew.

ISBN 0-17-612180-3

Science — Problems, exercises, etc. I. LeDrew, Barry. II. Title: Science 9: concepts and connections

Q161.2.N45 2002 Suppl. 1   500
C2002-904393-X

Reviewers

Contents

Unit 1 Exploring Matter

Challenge   1
Getting Started: What Do You Already Know?   2
Getting Started: Try This Activity   3

1.1 Activity: Safety and Science
Report   6
Questions   10

1.2 Physical and Chemical Properties
Extension Activity   13
Questions   14

1.3 Physical and Chemical Changes
Try This Activity   16
Questions   17

1.4 Investigation: Observing Changes
Report   19
Questions   21

1.5 Everyday Chemical Changes
Try This Activity   23
Questions   25

1.6 Explore an Issue: "Xtreme" Chemical Changes
Debate   27
Questions   30

1.7 Career Profile: Hair Colourist
Questions   32

1.8 Models of Matter
Extension Activity   33
Questions   35

Unit 1: What Have You Learned So Far?   37

1.9 Classifying Matter
Extension Activity   38
Try This Activity   39
Questions   40

1.10 Mineral Extraction and Refining in Canada
Extension Activity   43
Questions   45

1.11 Investigation: Classifying Elements
Report   48
Questions   50

Unit 1: What Have You Learned So Far? 52

1.12 Putting Metals to Work
Questions   53

1.13 Atoms—The Inside Story
Questions   55

1.14 Chemical Symbols and Formulas
Extension Activity   57
Questions   59

1.15 Compounds and Molecules
Questions   61

1.16 Activity: Building Molecules
Report   64
Questions   67

1.17 Investigation: Black Box Atoms
Report   69
Questions   72

1.18 Organizing the Elements
Extension Activity   74
Questions   79

1.19 Activity: Exploring the Modern Periodic Table
Report   81
Questions   85

1.20 Case Study: Elemental Magic
Report   87
Try This Activity   89
Questions   90

Summary: What Have You Learned?   94
Summary: Concept Map   95
Challenge Journal   97

Unit 2: Reproduction: Processes and Applications

Challenge 101
Getting Started: What Do You Already
 Know? 102
Getting Started: Try This Activity 105

2.1 The Importance of Cell Division
Try This Activity 106
Questions 107

2.2 Cell Division
Alternate Activity 109
Questions 112

2.3 Activity: Observing Cell Division
Report 114
Questions 116

**2.4 Case Study: Cell Division
and Growth**
Report 118
Questions 120

2.5 Cancer
Questions 122

2.6 Activity: Lifestyle and Cancer
Report 125
Questions 130

**2.7 Explore an Issue: Search for the
Fountain of Youth**
Debate 132
Questions 134

Unit 2: What Have You Learned
 So Far? 135

2.8 Cell Division and Reproduction
Try This Activity 136
Questions 138

2.9 Asexual Reproduction: Cloning
Questions 142

**2.10 Investigation: Cloning from
Plant Cuttings**
Report 145
Questions 148

2.11 Sexual Reproduction
Extension Activity 151
Questions 152

**2.12 Investigation: Sexual Reproduction
in Plants**
Report 154
Questions 156

**2.13 Case Study: Reproduction of Plants
for Food**
Report 158
Try This Activity 160
Questions 161

2.14 Career Profile: Horticulturist
Questions 163

**2.15 Reproductive Strategies for
Survival**
Extension Activity 165
Questions 168

Unit 2: What Have You Learned
 So Far? 171

2.16 Human Sex Cell Development
Questions 172

**2.17 Human Conception and
Implantation**
Extension Investigation 174
Questions 177

2.18 Human Reproductive Technology
Questions 179

2.19 Pregnancy and Birth
Extension Activity 182
Questions 185

**2.20 Explore an Issue: Fetal Alcohol
Syndrome**
Take a Stand 189
Questions 191

Summary: What Have You Learned? 192
Summary: Concept Map 193
Challenge Journal 195

Unit 3 Electrical Applications

Challenge   199
Getting Started: What Do You Already
  Know?   200
Getting Started: Try This Activity   203

**3.1 Investigation: Investigating
Electric Charges**
Report   205
Questions   207

3.2 Electricity and Matter
Questions   210

3.3 Investigation: Charging by Contact
Report   212
Questions   215

3.4 What Is Electric Current?
Try This Activity   217
Questions   219

3.5 Activity: The Electric Circuit
Report   221
Questions   226

3.6 Series and Parallel Circuits
Extension Activity   229
Questions   231

Unit 3: What Have You Learned
  So Far?   234

**3.7 Investigation: Building Parallel and
Series Circuits**
Report   235
Questions   237

**3.8 Measuring Voltage Drop
and Current**
Questions   239

**3.9 Investigation: Comparing Current
and Voltage Drop in an Electric Circuit**
Report   241
Questions   245

3.10 Case Study: Electrical Resistance
Report   246
Try This Activity   248
Questions   249

**3.11 Investigation: The Effect of
Resistance on an Electric Circuit**
Report   252
Questions   256

**3.12 Career Profile: Home Security
Systems Installer**
Questions   258

3.13 The Safe Use of Electricity
Extension Activity   260
Questions   262

Unit 3: What Have You Learned
  So Far?   265

3.14 Energy Conservation
Extension Activity   266
Try This Activity   267
Questions   269

3.15 Activity: The Family Energy Audit
Report   271
Questions   274

3.16 Efficiency and Electrical Devices
Questions   276

**3.17 Case Study: Automobiles and the
Fuel Cell**
Report   278
Questions   280

**3.18 Comparing Electrical Energy
Production**
Try This Activity   281
Questions   282

**3.19 Explore an Issue: Choosing an
Energy Source**
Take a Stand   286
Questions   288

**3.20 Activity: Building a Home
Wiring Model**
Report   289
Questions   291

Summary: What Have You Learned?   292
Summary: Concept Map   293
Challenge Journal   295

Unit 4 Space Exploration

Challenge   299
Getting Started: What Do You Already
  Know?   300
Getting Started: Try This Activity   301

4.1 What Can We See in the Sky?
Extension Activity   302
Extension Activity   303
Questions   304

4.2 Planets on the Move
Try This Activity   305
Questions   306

4.3 Case Study: Different Views of the Sky
Report   307
Questions   309

4.4 Activity: A Seasonal Star Map
Extension Activity   311
Report   313
Questions   314

4.5 The Planets in the Solar System
Questions   316

4.6 Investigation: Planets and Retrograde Motion
Report   318
Questions   320

4.7 Other Objects in the Solar System
Extension Activity   322
Try This Activity   324
Questions   325

Unit 4: What Have You Learned
  So Far?   327

4.8 Case Study: Telescopes
Extension Activity   328
Report   329
Questions   330

4.9 Career Profile: Space Artist
Questions   331

4.10 Case Study: The Sun: An Important Star
Report   332
Try This Activity   334
Questions   336

4.11 Galaxies and Star Clusters
Extension Activity   338
Try This Activity   339
Questions   340

4.12 Investigation: Flame Tests
Report   341
Questions   342

4.13 Evidence of an Expanding Universe
Try This Activity   344
Questions   345

4.14 Activity: A Model of the Expanding Universe
Extension Activity   347
Try This Activity   348
Report   349
Questions   350

4.15 The Origin of the Universe
Extension Activity   351
Try This Activity   354
Questions   355

Unit 4: What Have You Learned
  So Far?   357

4.16 Case Study: Satellites
Report   358
Try This Activity   359
Questions   360

4.17 The International Space Station
Try This Activity   362
Questions   363

4.18 Humans in Space
Try This Activity   364
Questions   365

4.19 Activity: Spinoffs of the Space Program
Report   367
Questions   369

4.20 Explore an Issue: Our Future in Space
Extension Activity   370
Take a Stand   371
Questions   373

Summary: What Have You Learned?   374
Summary: Concept Map   375
Challenge Journal   377

Challenge

Exploring Matter

As you learn about elements and compounds, you will learn about ways to explain the behaviour of matter. You will also be able to demonstrate your learning by completing one of the following Challenges.

1 Marketing Matter

Create a proposal that promotes a new material to a manufacturing company. Make sure to identify any raw materials that were used to make this new material, describe the process that was used to make the new material, and identify any risks associated with the use of this new material.

2 Time Capsule

Choose an artifact for a time capsule. The artifact should be a sample of a modern material, a sample of a material whose properties are easily recognized, and represented by a model to explain the structure of the material and its properties.

3 A Famous Scientist

Choose a famous scientist who discovered one of the elements, and for that person write a journal entry from when she or he was in high school and an obituary.

Choose a Challenge. Use the space on pages 98–100 to answer the Challenge questions from your text and to record your ideas for your challenge.

How I Am Being Assessed _____

_____

1. What are some of the different ways that matter can be organized or classified?

   _____

   _____

   _____

2. With a partner or in a small group, list as many changes in matter as you can. Use a different action word for each change (for example, a hot dog *cooks*, snow *melts*).
   (a) In which changes do you think a new substance formed?
   (b) In which changes do you think matter is added to the air?

Change	New substance? (√)	Matter added to air? (√)

3. Models are used in science to help you see and understand an idea or concept.

   (a) What scientific models are you already familiar with?

   _____

   _____

   _____

   (b) Choose one scientific model. What does it explain?

   _____

   _____

| How I Am Being Assessed _____ |
| _____ |

Fill a Balloon Using Chemistry

(a) Describe each substance.

baking soda: _____

vinegar:_____

(b) What happened when the two substances were mixed?

_____

_____

(c) Draw a diagram and explain how you blew up the balloon without using your breath.

_____

_____

_____

_____

_____

_____

_____

_____

_____

(d) How much did your balloon expand compared with other groups' balloons?

_____

_____

(e) Using the same quantities, what change(s) would you make to get maximum expansion?

_____

_____

_____

_____

Think back to what you learned in earlier grades.

Complete as much as you can of the concept map below. At the end of the unit, come back to this page and
  (a) add to the concept map.
  (b) correct any information that may not be accurate.

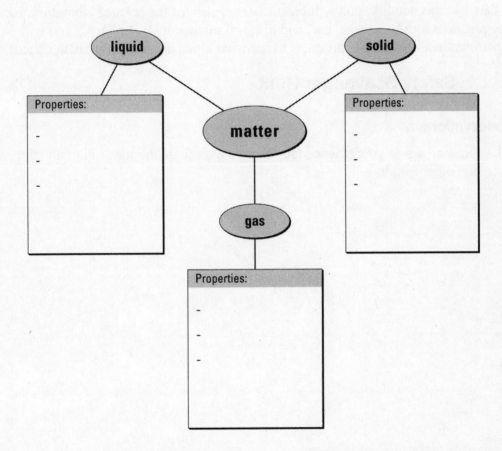

1.1 Activity
Safety and Science

Report

How I Am Being Assessed _____

_____

In Part 1 of this activity, you will create safety rules for the science laboratory, including safe practices for the storage, use, and disposal of chemicals. In Part 2, you will experiment with household products to see what kinds of changes in matter occur.

Part 1: Safety Scavenger Hunt

Observations

1. Draw a map of your science lab. Be sure to include the location of all lab benches and other furniture.

2. Locate each of the following safety devices. Indicate, using the letter, the corresponding location on your map.

   A   fire extinguisher
   B   fire blanket
   C   closest fire alarm
   D   safety goggles
   E   aprons
   F   eyewash station
   G   disposal container for broken glass
   H   disposal container for chemicals
   I   intercom or closest telephone

3. Examine the samples of chemicals and household products provided. Complete the table.

Name of product	Active ingredient (from label)	Warning symbol	Nature of hazard

4. Refer to the Skills Handbook at the back of the textbook. With your partner, discuss and write a safety rule, or direction, for each of the following situations as they apply to laboratory activity:

Laboratory situation	Safety rule or direction
eye protection	
clothing protection	
burns, cuts, or injuries	
allergies	
broken glass	
waste or spilled chemicals	
skin contact with a corrosive chemical	
chemicals splashed into the eyes	
damaged equipment	
heating chemicals	
smelling chemicals	
fooling around, paying too little attention	
food and drink	
out-of-school investigations	
living things	

Part 2: Kitchen Chemistry

Observations

(a)-(c) Use this table to record your observations.

Kitchen chemical pair	Initial observations	Changes when they mix
vinegar + table salt	vinegar: table salt:	
vinegar + starch	vinegar: starch:	
vinegar + baking soda	vinegar: baking soda:	
iodine + table salt	iodine: table salt:	
iodine + starch	iodine: starch:	
iodine + baking soda	iodine: baking soda:	
water + table salt	water: table salt:	
water + starch	water: starch:	
water + baking soda	water: baking soda:	

Analysis and Conclusion

(d) Which substances caused a change in the table salt? During which change, if any, was a new substance formed?

_____

_____

_____

(e) What changes did you observe in the starch? Was a new substance formed during any of the changes?

_____

_____

_____

(f) Consider the data you collected for the baking soda. Do any of your observations suggest that a new substance has formed? Explain.

_____

_____

_____

_____

1.1 Activity: Safety and Science **9**

1.1 Activity
Safety and Science

How I Am Being Assessed _____

_____

Understanding Concepts

1. Why is it important to use a standard set of safety symbols when labelling substances

    (a) in the home?

    _____

    _____

    (b) in the science laboratory or the workplace?

    _____

    _____

2. Briefly describe what you would do if any corrosive chemical you were using came in contact with bare skin on your arm.

    _____

    _____

    _____

3. Do you think it is always safe to pour waste chemicals down the sink with lots of water? Why or why not?

    _____

    _____

    _____

Making Connections

4. **(a)** Why do body shop employees wear a facemask when painting a car?

    _____

    _____

10 *Unit 1   Exploring Matter*   Copyright © 2003 Nelson

(b) Why do hairdressers wear rubber gloves when colouring or chemically straightening hair?

_____

_____

(c) Why do firefighters wear a breathing apparatus and protective clothing when entering a burning building?

_____

_____

Exploring

5. Locate containers in your home that have HHPS symbols on the labels.

(a) According to the symbol and information on the label, is each container and its contents stored safely? (Are flammable materials stored away from heat sources, for example?)

_____

_____

_____

(b) Do any containers in your home have WHMIS symbols on the labels? If so, how do you suppose they got there?

_____

_____

_____

(c) Prepare an action plan for safely disposing of these products.

_____

_____

_____

_____

_____

_____

1.1 Activity: Safety and Science **11**

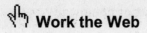 **Work the Web**

Look at a Material Safety Data Sheet (MSDS). List the information that is on the sheet. What is the importance of this sheet? Why aren't only WHMIS labels used?

_____

_____

_____

_____

_____

_____

_____

_____

_____

_____

_____

_____

_____

_____

How I Am Being Assessed _____

_____

Physical Properties

Refer to **Table 1** on page 14 of your text. Your teacher will give your class several different materials. Choose one. In the space below, describe as many physical properties of the material as you can.

Material: _____

Physical properties:

_____

_____

_____

_____

_____

_____

_____

_____

1.2 Physical and Chemical Properties

Questions

How I Am Being Assessed _____

_____

Understanding Concepts

1. What property is described by each of the following statements?

    (a) A steel blade can scratch glass. _____

    (b) Water boils at 100°C. _____

    (c) Alcohol is flammable. _____

2. Give one physical and one chemical property of

    (a) a marshmallow: _____

    (b) a hot dog: _____

    (c) an egg: _____

Making Connections

3. The top of a glass container of drinking water breaks, and some pieces of glass fall into the container. What physical property of glass would help you to separate the broken glass from the water?

    _____

    _____

    _____

Exploring

4. Find out about the disaster of the airship Hindenburg.

   (a) What gas was used to inflate the airship? What property of this gas contributed to its disaster?

   _____

   _____

   (b) What gas is used to inflate airships today? What property of this gas makes it safer?

   _____

   _____

1.3 Physical and Chemical Changes

How I Am Being Assessed _____

_____

List your observations of the candle in this table.

Unlit candle	Burning candle	Extinguished candle
qualitative (senses):	qualitative (senses):	qualitative (senses):
quantitative (measurements):	quantitative (measurements):	quantitative (measurements):

1.3 Physical and Chemical Changes

How I Am Being Assessed _____
_____

Understanding Concepts

1. Explain in your own words how a physical change and a chemical change are different.

_____

_____

_____

_____

2. Identify each of the following as a physical or chemical change. Explain your choice.

Example	Physical or chemical change?	Why?
(a) shattering glass		
(b) baking cookies in the oven		
(c) lights left on in a room		
(d) burning leaves in the fall		

Making Connections

3. Why should you never operate a gas or charcoal barbecue inside your home?

_____

_____

_____

Reflecting

4. Look at your observation table for Part 2: Kitchen Chemistry in section 1.1. Which combinations of kitchen chemicals produced physical changes, and which produced chemical changes?

Combination	Physical or chemical change?
vinegar + table salt	
vinegar + starch	
vinegar + baking soda	
iodine + table salt	
iodine + starch	
iodine + baking soda	
water + table salt	
water + starch	
water + baking soda	

How I Am Being Assessed _____

_____

In this investigation, you will observe changes in chemical substances and identify which are physical and which are chemical.

Question

How can you recognize a chemical change as different from a physical change?

Observations

(a)-(f) Record your observations in the table.

Before mixing (original substances)	Mixed	After mixing
baking soda	baking soda + phenol red	baking soda + calcium chloride + phenol red
calcium chloride	calcium chloride + phenol red	
phenol red solution		

Analysis and Conclusion

(g) What kind of change took place when you mixed the substances together in step 5? Explain.

_____

_____

_____

(h) What kind of change took place when you mixed the substances together in step 6? Explain.

_____

_____

_____

(i) What kind of change took place in step 7? Explain.

_____

_____

(j) At any point in the procedure, did you observe a physical change? If so, when?

_____

_____

(k) Use the evidence in your observation table to make a list of the clues that you can use to recognize a chemical change.

_____

_____

_____

1.4 Investigation Observing Changes

How I Am Being Assessed _____
_____

Understanding Concepts

1. Classify each of the following as a physical or a chemical change. Explain your decision.

Example	Physical or chemical?	Reason
(a) rotting garbage		
(b) cutting up vegetables for a meal		
(c) a silver necklace leaving a mark on your skin		
(d) cooking an egg		
(e) bleaching a stain out of your clothing		

Making Connections

2. List three examples of physical changes and three examples of chemical changes that you have observed at home. For each example, give a reason for your decision.

physical changes

_____

_____

_____

chemical changes

_____

_____

_____

🖐 Work the Web

Find out what makes the best container for chemical reactions. From the information you find, choose the best container to use as a time capsule, and collect data to support your choice.

_____

_____

_____

_____

_____

_____

_____

_____

_____

How I Am Being Assessed _____

_____

Preventing Corrosion

You work for a small corrosion laboratory. Your company has a contract to investigate ways to prevent the corrosion of aluminum, magnesium, and steel metals. Your team is assigned to investigate and compare the effectiveness of two methods of preventing corrosion: painting and oiling.

- Design a test, including safety procedures, to compare the effectiveness of paint and oil in protecting metals from corrosion.

Procedure

1. _____

   _____

2. _____

   _____

3. _____

   _____

4. _____

   _____

5. _____

   _____

Observations

Record your observations and answer to questions (a) and (b) in this table.

Metals	Initial observations	Changes
aluminum		
magnesium		
steel (iron)		

(c) Was your experimental design a fair test? Explain.

_____

_____

_____

(d) Was paint or oil more effective in preventing corrosion? Use your observations to explain your answer.

_____

_____

_____

(e) What changes would you make to the experimental design? With your teacher's permission, try them.

_____

_____

_____

(f) Present your results in a report to be distributed to companies that manufacture aluminum, magnesium, and steel.

_____

_____

_____

_____

_____

_____

How I Am Being Assessed _____

_____

Understanding Concepts

1. What is corrosion?

   _____

   _____

   _____

   _____

2. How is iron oxide formed?

   _____

   _____

   _____

3. Describe three ways to protect a metal from corrosion.

   _____

   _____

   _____

4. (a) Which parts of a car corrode the most? Why?

   _____

   _____

   _____

   (b) How can car owners help to reduce the effects of corrosion?

   _____

   _____

   _____

Making Connections

5. List objects in your home that can corrode. What steps can you take to protect these items from corrosion?

Object   Prevent Corrosion

_____   _____

_____   _____

_____   _____

_____   _____

_____   _____

_____   _____

Work the Web

Find additional ways of preventing rust and corrosion.

_____

_____

_____

_____

_____

_____

_____

_____

_____

1.6 Explore an Issue
"Xtreme" Chemical Changes

Debate

How I Am Being Assessed _____

_____

Should fireworks be banned?

To help you decide which view to support, use the following table to write the reasons you agree or disagree with each view.

View	Why I agree with this view	Why I disagree with this view
Fireworks are dangerous, polluting, and a waste of money and should be banned within city boundaries.		
Fireworks are a good tradition, promote tourism, and are financially beneficial and should not be banned within city boundaries. It would be more dangerous to have people using fireworks outside the city, where the risks can be greater.		

In the space below, create a concept map showing your point of view on the issue and all the points that support it. Make sure to add at least two ideas of your own to your map.

My position on the issue is

_____

_____

_____

The reasons for my decision are

_____

_____

_____

_____

_____

_____

_____

How I Am Being Assessed _____

_____

Understanding Concepts

1. Explain how fireworks give off bursts of light and sound.

_____

_____

_____

_____

_____

2. What does an oxidizer do?

_____

_____

_____

_____

_____

_____

3. Why are oxidizers so dangerous?

_____

_____

_____

_____

_____

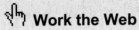 **Work the Web**

Colour	Salts used
red	
orange	
gold	
yellow	
electric white	
green	
blue	
purple	
silver	

What do pyrotechnic technicians need to get pure colours?

_____

_____

_____

_____

_____

_____

How I Am Being Assessed

Making Connections

1. Find out whether there are any courses for hairstylists at your school or at a nearby school. What are the requirements, if any, to get into the course? How long is the training?

_____

_____

2. Are there any advantages to taking an apprenticeship program? Explain.

_____

_____

Reflecting

3. A customer asks you to colour his dark brown hair with "dark blond" tips. How would you get him to tell you exactly what he wanted before you begin?

_____

_____

🖑 Work the Web

There are two basic types of hair colour: temporary and permament. Find out how they differ chemically.

_____

_____

_____

How does each affect hair?

_____

_____

1.8 Models of Matter   *Extension Activity*

Separating Mixtures

In this activity, you will be given a mixture of salt, sand, and iron pellets. Each part of the mixture will be clearly visible in the sample. Your task is to separate the mixture into its three separate parts.

Question

How would you separate the parts of a heterogeneous mixture based on the properties of the parts?

Prediction

(a) Write a prediction based on the question above.

_____

_____

_____

Materials

Make a list of the materials and equipment that you will need to separate the mixture into its parts.

_____   _____

_____   _____

_____   _____

Procedure

Design a test that you will follow to separate the parts of this mixture. Be sure to get your teacher's approval before you begin the test.

1. _____

_____

2. _____

_____

3. _____

_____

4. _____

_____

5. _____

_____

6. _____

_____

Analysis and Conclusion

(b) What property did you use to separate the salt from the mixture? Explain.

_____

_____

(c) What property did you use to separate the sand from the mixture? Explain.

_____

_____

(d) What property did you use to separate the iron pellets from the mixture? Explain.

_____

_____

(e) During the separation process, where did you observe

(i) an element? _____

(ii) a compound? _____

(iii) a solution? _____

(f) Was your prediction correct? Explain why or why not based on your observations.

_____

_____

How I Am Being Assessed _____

_____

Understanding Concepts

1. Use a diagram to illustrate and explain the difference between a pure substance and a mixture.

pure substance	mixture

_____

_____

_____

2. Give two examples of molecules that are made from the same kind of atom. Which compounds do they represent?

_____

_____

Making Connections

3. Complete **Table 1** by filling in the middle column. Choose from

   (i) pure substance—element

   (ii) pure substance—compound

   (iii) mixture

Table 1

Name of substance	Type of substance	Description
table salt		white crystalline solid
orange juice		mixture of juice and pulp
copper		reddish-brown wire
iron		coarse black powder
salad dressing		oil and vinegar

4. Now that you know that atoms and molecules are the "particles" in the particle model, do you think that atoms can be broken down into smaller particles? Explain.

_____

_____

_____

_____

How I Am Being Assessed _____

_____

Complete the graphic organizer below to summarize the key concepts presented to this point.

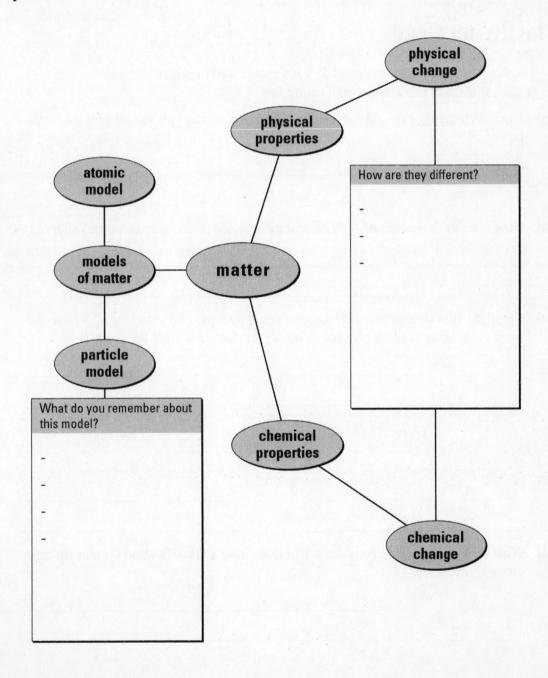

How I Am Being Assessed _____

_____

> Make your teacher aware of any known allergies you have to any of the ingredients (check the labels!) in the candy bars provided for this activity.

Classifying Candy

- Examine the candy bars assigned to your group, and organize them into categories.
- Break off a small piece from each candy bar.

(a) Does each candy bar look the same throughout, or can you see other substances mixed in?

_____

_____

(b) How is a bar that contains only chocolate labelled differently from the others?

_____

_____

(c) Compare your categories with those of other groups. Did your group choose the same categories as other groups? Would you change yours? Why or why not?

_____

_____

Ours   Theirs

_____   _____

_____   _____

_____   _____

(d) What things would you consider when designing a classification system for any group of items?

_____

_____

1.9 Classifying Matter   *Try This Activity*

How I Am Being Assessed _____

_____

Classification

In this activity, pick one of the following places and describe how the items are organized there. Your description may be a paragraph or a labelled sketch.

- the place where you keep your clothes (for example, a chest of drawers, a closet)
- the place where food is kept in your home (for example, cupboards)
- your favourite music store
- your favourite clothing store

_____

_____

_____

_____

_____

_____

_____

(a) For the place that you chose to investigate, name the categories into which items were sorted.

_____   _____

_____   _____

_____   _____

(b) Did students who investigated the other choices observe the same categories? Why or why not?

_____

_____

_____

How I Am Being Assessed _____

_____

Understanding Concepts

1. **(a)** What is meant by the term "natural" when describing a substance? Give two examples.

   _____

   _____

   _____

   _____

   (b) What is meant by the term "synthetic substance"? Give two examples.

   _____

   _____

   _____

   _____

2. How are elements and compounds

   (a) the same?

   _____

   _____

   _____

   (b) different?

   _____

   _____

   _____

3. (a) What is a pure substance? Give an example.

_____

_____

_____

(b) What is a mixture? Give an example.

_____

_____

_____

4. Explain the difference between heterogeneous and homogeneous mixtures.

_____

_____

_____

_____

5. Give an example of a homogeneous mixture that is

(a) a solid.

_____

(b) a liquid.

_____

(c) a gas.

_____

Making Connections

6. The company you work for has asked your team to come up with a new mixture that can be made using two or more substances from the following list. Invent a use for your mixture.

Substance	Useful property
A	sticks to plastic
B	is bright blue
C	boils at 20°C
D	smells like bananas

E	is elastic
F	glows in the dark
G	conducts electricity
H	bends without breaking
I	repels insects

Mixture: _____

Use: _____

_____

_____

_____

✋ Work the Web

What were you able to find out about Joseph Priestly?

_____

_____

_____

_____

_____

_____

_____

_____

How I Am Being Assessed _____

_____

Mining for "Chocolate"

Ore is mined only if it is profitable to do so. After the ore is removed from the rock face, the desired minerals, or elements, must be separated from the ore. There are many ways to do this. In all cases, the value of the mineral must always be greater than the cost of separating it from the ore—there must be a profit!

In this activity, you will simulate the separation process by exploring a method to separate the chocolate from chocolate chip cookies.

Materials

- 2 chocolate chip cookies (different brands)
- cocktail toothpick
- 5-cm lengths of plastic drinking straws

Procedure

1. Use the toothpick to remove the chocolate chips from both the top and bottom surfaces of each cookie.

2. Use your fingers to break the cookie into smaller pieces so that all the chocolate can be removed with the toothpick.

3. Record the time it takes to separate the chocolate from the cookie.

4. Repeat steps 1, 2, and 3 with a second cookie of a different brand.

5. Fill lengths of plastic drinking straw with chocolate to compare the amount of chocolate in each of the two brands of cookies.

Observations

Cookie A: amount of chocolate = _____ straw sections

Cookie B: amount of chocolate = _____ straw sections

Making Connections

1. Is it easier to remove the chocolate chips from the top of the cookie or from the bottom of the cookie? Why?

   _____

   _____

   _____

2. (a) Which brand of cookie contains the most chocolate? _____

   (b) Is comparing the amount of chocolate in one cookie from each brand a fair test? Explain.

   _____

   _____

   _____

   _____

3. Suppose workers who separate chocolate "mineral" from cookie "ore" are paid $20 an hour.

   (a) Based on how long it took you to separate the chocolate from one cookie, how much would you have been paid?

   _____

   _____

   (b) If each length of straw filled with chocolate has a market value of $10, was your mineral separation profitable? Why or why not?

   _____

   _____

   _____

4. If your separation was not profitable, what could you do to make it profitable?

   _____

   _____

   _____

   _____

Understanding Concepts

1. (a) Use **Table 1** on page 32 of your text to write the mineral or chemical formula for each of the following:

    (i)   bauxite _____

    (ii) cinnabar _____

    (iii) galena _____

    (b) Identify the desired element in each mineral.

    (i)   bauxite _____

    (ii) cinnabar _____

    (iii) galena _____

2. Name three elements that occur as pure substances in nature.

    _____

    _____

    _____

3. List four steps that are required to separate an element from the ore in which it is found.

    _____

    _____

    _____

    _____

Exploring

4. Research the methods used to obtain one of the following elements in Canada: nickel, copper, aluminum, iron, gold. Prepare a Bristol board presentation of the information you were able to find.

Element: _____

_____

_____

_____

_____

_____

_____

_____

5. Many communities collect aluminum beverage cans at the curbside for recycling.

(a) Is recycling a good alternative to using raw aluminum?

_____

_____

_____

(b) How does the cost of recycling compare with the cost of extracting aluminum from the ground?

_____

_____

_____

(c) Which process results in fewer environmental problems?

_____

_____

_____

(d) Use the answers to (a)–(c) to decide whether recycling is a reasonable alternative for producing aluminum beverage cans.

_____

_____

_____

_____

_____

_____

_____

1.11 Investigation
Classifying Elements

Report

In this investigation, you will examine whether a number of elements can be grouped according to the properties they have in common.

Question

Can elements be grouped by properties they share?

Prediction

(a) Predict which elements should be classified together. Explain your groupings.

_____

_____

Observations

(b)-(e) Record your observations in **Table 1**.

Table 1

Element	Properties					
	Colour	Lustre	Hardness	Density	Magnetic	Other
1.						
2.						
3.						
4.						
5.						
6.						
7.						
8.						
9.						
10.						

(f) Record your observations in **Table 2**.

Table 2: **Electrical Conductivity**

Element	Electrical conductor (√)
1.	
2.	
3.	
4.	
5.	
6.	
7.	
8.	
9.	
10.	

Analysis and Conclusion

(g) Based on your observations, can you group the sample elements into categories according to their properties? If you can, how many categories can you use?

_____

_____

_____

_____

(h) For each category you chose in (g), list the elements that you would place in each category. How are the elements in one category the same or different from the elements in the other categories?

_____

_____

_____

_____

_____

1.11 Investigation

Classifying Elements

Questions

How I Am Being Assessed _____

_____

Making Connections

1. How do the properties of the following elements determine their use?

   (a) Copper and aluminum were both used in electrical wiring at one time.

   _____

   _____

   (b) Carbon rods are used in some batteries.

   _____

   _____

   (c) Steel (iron) cans can be separated easily from aluminum cans.

   _____

   _____

2. You may have noticed that when you put certain solid objects against your skin they feel cold.

   (a) Why does this happen?

   _____

   _____

   (b) What physical property explains this observation?

   _____

   _____

(c) Describe how an element with this property might be used.

_____

_____

☞ Work the Web

How do other classification systems of elements that you find compare with the groupings you have determined in this investigation?

_____

_____

_____

_____

_____

_____

_____

_____

How I Am Being Assessed _____

_____

Complete the graphic organizer below.

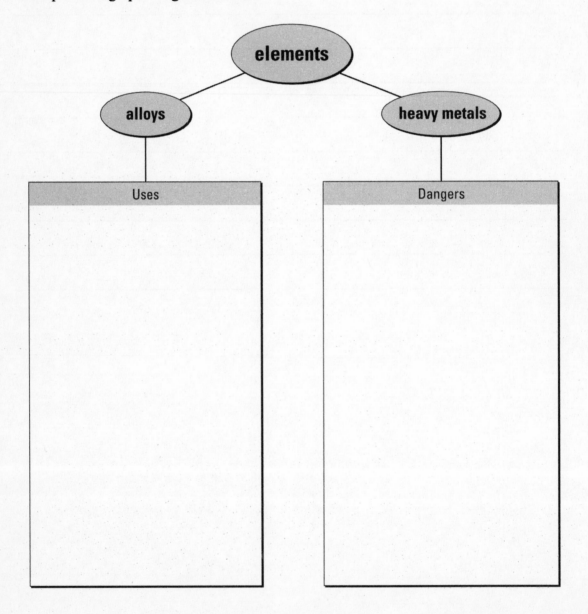

1.12 Putting Metals to Work   *Questions*

How I Am Being Assessed _____

_____

Understanding Concepts

1. Name two properties that would be required of a metal used for braces for teeth.

    _____

    _____

2. Name a metal that is

    (a) a good conductor of heat   _____

    (b) used to make jewellery   _____

    (c) no longer a part of gasoline   _____

    (d) no longer in many paint products   _____

    (e) used to make tire rims   _____

3. Identify three chemicals that are needed in large amounts by plants.

    _____

    _____

Making Connections

4. If you were to eat mercury-contaminated fish, what would likely be the

   (a) short-term effect?

     _____

     _____

     _____

   (b) long-term effect?

     _____

     _____

     _____

Work the Web

Describe one use for each alloy that you find. What properties does the alloy have that make it suitable for this use?

	Component metals	Use for alloy	Properties of alloy
alloy 1			
alloy 2			
alloy 3			
alloy 4			
alloy 5			

How I Am Being Assessed _____

_____

Understanding Concepts

1. Complete the following table:

Particle	Proton	Neutron	Electron
mass			
charge			
location in atom			

2. Write the standard atomic notation for:

   (a) an atom of nitrogen with 7 protons and 7 neutrons.

   _____

   (b) an atom of sulfur with 16 protons and 16 neutrons.

   _____

3. Draw Bohr-Rutherford diagrams for

   (a) oxygen (O): 8 protons, 8 neutrons

   (b) aluminum (Al): 13 protons, 14 neutrons

(c) sodium (Na): 11 protons, 12 neutrons

Bonus: Double Puzzle

Unscramble the words to find the hidden vocabulary word.

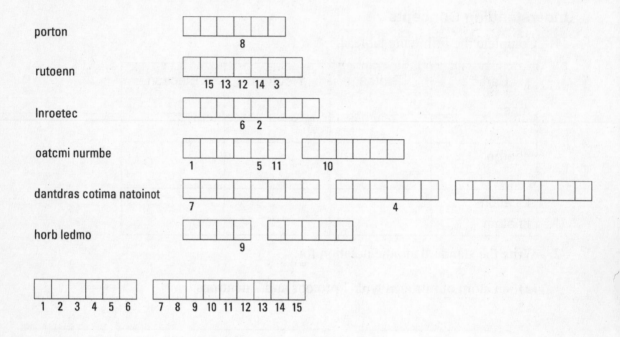

porton

rutoenn

lnroetec

oatcmi nurmbe

dantdras cotima natoinot

horb ledmo

How I Am Being Assessed _____
_____

Chemical Symbols

1. Write the symbols for the following elements. Use the periodic table at the back of your text.

    hydrogen: _____   magnesium: _____   chromium: _____

    sodium: _____   strontium: _____   iron: _____

    platinum: _____   silver: _____   mercury: _____

    carbon: _____   tin: _____   nitrogen: _____

    oxygen: _____   fluorine: _____   bromine: _____

    helium: _____   chlorine: _____   krypton: _____

2. Use the following symbols to write the names of the elements:

    Li: _____   K: _____

    Ca: _____   Ba: _____

    Mn: _____   Ni: _____

    Cu: _____   Zn: _____

    Al: _____   Si: _____

    Pb: _____   P: _____

    S: _____   Cl: _____

    I: _____   Ne: _____

Counting Atoms

3. For each compound, list the element and the number of atoms of each element found in the compound. The first one has been done for you.

Name	Formula	Common name	Number of elements	Atoms in formula
acetic acid	$C_2H_4O_2$	found in vinegar	3	C = carbon 2 H = hydrogen 4 O = oxygen 2
paradichlorobenzene	$C_6H_4O_2$	mothballs		
pyrite	FeS_3	fool's gold		
sucrose	$C_{12}H_{22}O_{11}$	table sugar		
butane	C_4H_{10}	lighter fluid		
asbestos	$H_4Mg_3Si_2O_9$	insulation		
ascorbic acid	$C_6H_8O_6$	vitamin C		
sulfuric acid	H_2SO_4	battery acid		
ethanol	CH_3CH_2OH	rubbing alcohol		

1.14 Chemical Symbols and Formulas

Questions

How I Am Being Assessed _____

_____

Understanding Concepts

1. Why are symbols useful in describing chemicals?

   _____

   _____

   _____

2. Use your periodic table at the back of your text to find the symbols for the following elements:

   lithium: _____   silicon: _____

   argon: _____   copper: _____

   phosphorous: _____   gold: _____

3. What two things does a chemical formula tell us about a compound?

   _____

   _____

4. Write a chemical formula for the following:

   (a) a molecule of carbon dioxide that is made up of one atom of carbon and two atoms of oxygen _____

   (b) a molecule of aspirin that is made up of nine atoms of carbon, eight atoms of hydrogen, and four atoms of oxygen _____

   (c) a molecule of sugar (glucose) that is made up of 6 atoms of carbon, 12 atoms of hydrogen, and 6 atoms of oxygen _____

Making Connections

5. Research a common use for each of the following pure substances:

   (a) helium gas

   _____

   _____

   _____

   _____

   (b) acetone

   _____

   _____

   _____

   _____

   (c) tartaric acid

   _____

   _____

   _____

   _____

Work the Web

Match the element with its symbol. Compare answers with a partner.

Element	Symbol

_____ number correct

1.15 Compounds and Molecules *Questions*

Understanding Concepts

1. What does the term "combining capacity" mean?

   _____

   _____

   _____

2. Elements can be classified as metals or nonmetals. Which elements change their names when they form compounds? Explain, using an example.

   _____

   _____

   _____

   _____

3. What are the names of the following compounds?

   (a) $CaCl_2$, used in bleaching powder and for melting ice: _____

   (b) CaO, used in plaster and construction: _____

   (c) $CuCl$, used to make red glass: _____

   (d) $AgCl$, used in photography: _____

4. Use the combining capacities shown in **Tables 2** and **3** on page 42 of your text to write chemical formulas for

   (a) sodium fluoride: _____

   (b) magnesium fluoride: _____

   (c) potassium bromide: _____

   (d) silver oxide: _____

   (e) aluminum sulfide: _____

5. Draw "hook-and-ball" diagrams for the compounds in question 4.

(a)

(b)

(c)

(d)

(e)

6. Which of the following is not a compound? Why?

(a) CH_4 (b) H_2O

(c) NH_4 (d) N_2

_____

_____

Work the Web

Learn more about the way that elements bond together to form compounds.

_____

_____

_____

_____

_____

_____

_____

_____

_____

_____

1.16 Activity
Building Molecules
Report

In this activity, you will build models of some common molecules and see how bonds can link atoms in molecules.

(a) Draw a structural diagram of the molecule, H_2. Write the name and formula.

Name _____   Formula _____

(b) Draw a structural diagram of the molecule, O_2. Write the name and formula.

Name _____   Formula _____

(c) Draw structural diagrams of the models. Write the name and formula of each molecule.

Name _____   Formula_____

Name _____   Formula_____

Name _____   Formula_____

Name _____   Formula_____

Name _____   Formula_____

Name _____   Formula_____

(d) Draw structural diagrams of the models. Write the name and formula of each molecule.

Name _____   Formula_____

Name _____   Formula_____

Name _____   Formula_____

Name _____   Formula_____

Name _____   Formula_____

Name _____   Formula_____

How I Am Being Assessed _____

_____

Understanding Concepts

1. What is a model?

_____

_____

_____

2. Why do scientists find making models useful?

_____

_____

_____

3. Usually more bonds between two atoms make a stronger connection. Which of all the molecules you made probably has the strongest bond? Explain your reasoning.

_____

_____

_____

Making Connections

4. How are the marshmallow models like real molecules?

_____

_____

_____

5. How are the marshmallow models different from real molecules?

_____

_____

_____

Draw and colour a molecule of your choice. Label or describe what you are seeing.

1.17 Investigation
Black Box Atoms

How I Am Being Assessed _____

_____

In this investigation, you will try to guess what is inside a sealed box.

Black Box # _____

Question

How can we use a model to explain what we cannot see?

Prediction

(a) Write a prediction for this investigation.

_____

_____

_____

_____

Observations

(b)-(g) Use this table to record your observations.

Physical properties	Observations
outside dimensions	length: _____ cm width: _____ cm height: _____ cm
magnetic (yes/no)	
mass of empty box	
mass of black box	
mass of object(s) in black box	

shape	

(h) Write a description (or model) of what you think the object(s) is/are. For example, describing an object as "a 15-cm long metal object, branched into four small projections at one end" is better than describing it as a "fork."

_____

_____

_____

_____

(i) Make a drawing of what you think is in your "black box." Draw the object(s) to show their relative size.

Analysis and Conclusion

After completing your description and drawing, open the box and look at the object(s).

(j) Write a description of the object(s).

_____

_____

_____

_____

(k) Make a drawing of the contents of the box.

(l) How does your first prediction and drawing compare with the actual contents of the box? Was your prediction correct? Explain why or why not, based on your observations.

_____

_____

_____

_____

_____

(m) Describe how you can develop a model of an object without directly observing the object.

_____

_____

_____

_____

_____

_____

1.17 Investigation
Black Box Atoms

Questions

How I Am Being Assessed _____

_____

Making Connections

1. Think about a gumball machine.

   (a) What experiments could you do to find out how the gumball machine operates?

   _____

   _____

   _____

   _____

   (b) Draw a model of how you think the machine operates.

Exploring

2. Your teacher has buried an object in a soft ball of modelling clay. Take the ball, and using a probe provided by your teacher, carefully insert it into the ball. Make a systematic series of probings. Record your observations, and make a model drawing to describe what is inside the clay "atom."

Observations

_____

_____

_____

_____

Drawing

Reflecting

3. Think about your group's success with determining the identity of the object(s) in the "black box." Is there any reason why you successfully determined some characteristics but not others? Explain.

_____

_____

_____

_____

_____

How I Am Being Assessed	_____
	_____

Inventing a Periodic Table

Mendeleev invented his periodic table by looking for patterns in the properties of different groups of elements. He looked for similarities that would allow him to classify elements into groups with similar properties. He knew that not all of the elements had been discovered, so he left spaces for them.

Imagine that you own a hardware store. You have received a shipment of nuts and bolts. Unfortunately, the contents have spilled and are all mixed together. You also suspect that some of the nuts or bolts are missing from your original order. You had planned to arrange the 20 different nuts and bolts in a logical pattern of four rows and five columns on a display rack.

What would be a logical arrangement? If one nut or bolt is missing, how would you predict its characteristics? In this activity, you will make a periodic table of nuts and bolts to answer these questions.

Materials

- balance
- ruler
- graph paper
- 19 nuts and bolts in a resealable plastic bag

Procedure

1. Obtain a bag of hardware items (nuts and bolts). There should be 19 items in the bag. Count them to make sure.

2. One item is missing from the shipment.

   (a) What nut or bolt do you think is missing? Describe it.

   _____

   _____

3. On the grid on the next page, number the squares from 1 to 20, starting in the left corner and numbering across the rows. Call these "hardware numbers."

4. With your group, invent a system that you will use to organize your nuts and bolts. Place each item in a square, leaving an empty space if necessary.

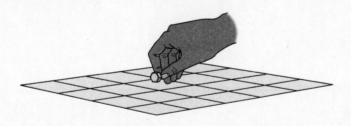

(b) Describe your organizing system.

_____

_____

_____

_____

_____

_____

5. Remove the nuts and bolts from the grid. Now, replace them on the grid using the following new system. Put the smallest bolt in the top left corner and the largest nut in the bottom right corner. Put similar items in the same vertical column. Arrange them so that size increases down each column and generally across each row.

(c) What nut or bolt do you now think is missing? Describe it.

_____

_____

_____

_____

6. Use the balance to measure the mass of each item.

(d) Record the masses in the appropriate squares in the grid.

7. Use a ruler to measure the longest dimension of each item.

(e) Record the lengths in the appropriate squares in the grid.

8. Count the nuts and bolts and return them to the bag.

9. Plot a graph of hardware mass versus hardware number (1–20).

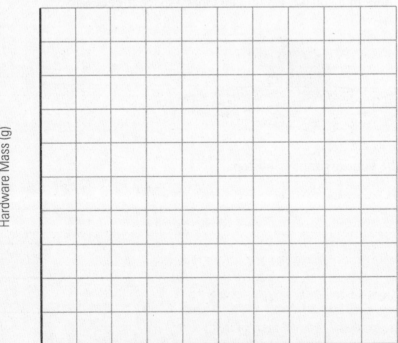

Hardware Number

10. Plot a graph of hardware length versus hardware number (1–20).

Hardware Length (mm)

Hardware Number

11. Examine your graph of mass versus number data.

(f) What general trend in mass do you see

(i) across any row of your table?

_____

_____

(ii) down any column of your table?

_____

_____

12. Examine your graph of length versus number data.

(g) What general trend in length do you see

(i) across any row of your table?

_____

_____

    (ii)   down any column of your table?

_____

_____

13. Predict the mass and length of the missing item.

_____

_____

_____

Questions

1. How does your hardware periodic table compare with Mendeleev's periodic table of elements?

_____

_____

_____

_____

2. What do you think the mass and length of the nuts and bolts could represent for atoms in Mendeleev's periodic table?

_____

_____

_____

_____

3. What group of elements do you think the nuts represent? Why?

_____

4. What groups of elements do you think the bolts represent? Why?

_____

5. Imagine that a nut and a bolt are screwed together. What do you think such a combination might represent?

_____

_____

_____

_____

How I Am Being Assessed _____

_____

Understanding Concepts

1. What are some of the properties that helped scientists organize elements into metals and nonmetals?

    _____

    _____

    _____

    _____

    _____

2. **(a)** What property of atoms did Mendeleev use to organize elements?

    _____

    (b) How did he use this property to organize them?

    _____

    _____

    _____

    (c) When did he ignore this property in building his table?

    _____

    _____

    _____

3. Explain why Mendeleev included spaces in his periodic table.

    _____

    _____

4. Why were properties such as colour and taste not used to arrange elements on the first periodic table?

_____

_____

_____

_____

5. Where on the modern periodic table do you find metals, nonmetals, and metalloids?

_____

_____

_____

_____

Work the Web

Make a list of Dmitri Mendeleev's scientific contributions other than the periodic table.

_____

_____

_____

_____

_____

_____

_____

_____

_____

_____

In this activity, you will work with a partner to find patterns or trends in the elements in the periodic table.

1. Look at the periodic table at the back of your text. The key at the top indicates the state at room temperature (solid, liquid, or gas) by the colour of the element's symbol. If the element's symbol is black, it is a solid. If the symbol is blue, the element is a liquid. If the symbol is red, it is a gas.

    (a) Which elements are gases at room temperature?

    _____

    _____

    (b) Name two elements that are liquids at room temperature.

    _____

2. Metals have a green background. Nonmetals have an orange background.

    (c) On which side of the table do you find the elements that are metals?

    _____

    (d) On which side of the table do you find the elements that are nonmetals?

    _____

    (e) Are most of the elements metals or nonmetals?

    _____

    (f) What are the elements called that have a purple background?

    _____

    (g) Why are they called that?

    _____

3. Find the names of the elements with the following chemical symbols:

H _____   Al _____

Fe _____   Eu _____

Kr _____   Xe _____

4. Find the chemical symbols for the following elements:

helium _____   iodine _____

lead _____   plutonium _____

uranium _____   einsteinium _____

5. Find the atomic numbers for the following elements:

Lr _____   Cs _____

Pt _____   Ag _____

He _____   Si _____

6. Find the atomic mass for the following elements:

sodium _____   zinc _____

chlorine _____   lithium _____

bromine _____   argon _____

7. Mendeleev used atomic masses to organize his periodic table. What two elements are "out of order" in the fifth row, according to atomic mass?

_____

8. Look at the densities and melting points of the elements.

(h) Which element has the highest melting temperature? What is it?

_____

(i) Which element has the lowest melting temperature? What is it?

_____

(j) Which element has the greatest density? What is it?

_____

(k) Which element has the lowest density? What is it?

_____

9. Elements 1, 3, 11, and 19 are in the first column of the periodic table.

(l) Draw Bohr-Rutherford diagrams for these elements. (Remember: the order of filling in the first three orbits is 2, 8, 8.)

hydrogen	lithium	sodium	potassium

(m) How many electrons are in the outer orbit of each of these elements? _____

(n) How many electrons do you think there are in the outer orbit of the elements Rb and Cs? _____

10. Elements 9 and 17 are in the second-last column of the periodic table.

(o) Draw Bohr-Rutherford diagrams for these elements.

fluorine	chlorine

(p) How many electrons are in the outer orbit of each of these elements? _____

(q) How many electrons do you think are in the outer orbit of the elements Br and I? _____

11. Look at elements 3 to 10.

    (r) Draw Bohr-Rutherford diagrams for these elements.

lithium	beryllium	boron	carbon
nitrogen	oxygen	fluorine	neon

    (s) Describe the general pattern (trend) that you observe across a row of the
        periodic table. (Hint: Look at the outer orbit of the electrons.)

    _____

    _____

    _____

    _____

12. Elements in the periodic table have been arranged in columns or groups according
    to their properties. Name four elements that have properties similar to lithium.

    _____

    _____

13. Helium is a gas that will not burn. Name three other gaseous elements that probably
    will not burn either.

    _____

    _____

1.19 Activity

Exploring the Modern Periodic Table

How I Am Being Assessed _____

_____

Understanding Concepts

1. At room temperature, in what state are most elements?

   _____

   _____

2. Using the word "increase" or "decrease," describe how the following properties generally change as you go across the rows (from left to right) of the periodic table:

   (a) atomic number

   _____

   _____

   (b) melting temperature

   _____

   _____

   (c) atomic radius

   _____

   _____

3. Using the word "increase" or "decrease," describe how the following properties generally change as you go down the columns (groups) of the periodic table:

   (a) density

   _____

   _____

(b) melting temperature

_____

_____

(c) atomic radius

_____

_____

Making Connections

4. Elements in the same group have similar properties. Think of two examples in everyday life where similar substances could be substituted for each other. What other factors would you consider before making the substitutions?

_____

_____

_____

_____

_____

Work the Web

Choose two elements, and write a short report comparing their properties and their uses.

_____

_____

_____

_____

_____

_____

_____

_____

_____

How I Am Being Assessed _____

_____

(a) What types of materials would likely have been used in 5000 B.C.E.?

_____

_____

_____

(b) What types of metals were being used in 1960?

_____

_____

_____

(c) What is the relationship between a monomer and a polymer?

_____

_____

_____

(d) What determines the properties of a polymer?

_____

_____

_____

(e) Give three examples of natural polymers.

_____

_____

_____

(f) Give three examples of synthetic polymers.

_____

_____

_____

(g) What is polymerization?

_____

_____

_____

(h) Carbon fibre, a ceramic, is used in sports equipment such as tennis racquets. What property does it have that makes it suitable for this use?

_____

_____

_____

(i) Paper is a composite. What substances might it contain?

_____

_____

_____

How I Am Being Assessed _____

_____

The Superball Polymer Goo Challenge

Borax (mL)	Water (mL)	Glue (mL)	Order of combining ingredients	Prediction of height of bounce	Actual height of bounce (cm)

How I Am Being Assessed _____

_____

Understanding Concepts

1. **(a)** Draw a bar graph to summarize the information in **Table 1** in your text.

Use (%)

Material

(b) Examine your graph. What types of materials were most important in

(i) 5000 B.C.E.?

_____

_____

_____

(ii) 1800?

_____

_____

_____

(iii) 1960?

_____

_____

_____

(iv) 2000?

_____

_____

_____

2. Give five examples of each type of material that you would use in a typical day.

   (a) polymers

   _____

   _____

   _____

   _____

   _____

   (b) ceramics

   _____

   _____

   _____

   _____

   (c) metals

   _____

   _____

   _____

   _____

   _____

(d) composites

_____

_____

_____

_____

_____

Making Connections

3. The development of almost indestructible polymers is not entirely good news. What drawbacks do they have?

_____

_____

_____

_____

_____

4. Polymers are used to make artificial body parts such as artificial knee joints and artificial hearts. What important properties do you think polymers used in artificial body parts must have?

_____

_____

_____

_____

_____

Work the Web

What are "Bucky-balls"? What makes them so important? What could they replace in computers? Draw a diagram of this molecule. What other information can you add?

_____

_____

_____

_____

_____

_____

_____

_____

_____

_____

_____

Diagram:

Unit 1 Summary
What Have You Learned?

How I Am Being Assessed _____

_____

Revisit your answers to the What Do You Already Know? questions on page 2 in the Getting Started.

Have any of your answers changed?

_____

_____

_____

_____

_____

_____

What new questions do you have?

_____

_____

_____

_____

_____

_____

_____

_____

How I Am Being Assessed _____

_____

Use the concept map to review the major concepts in Unit 1. This map can help you begin to organize the information that you have studied. You may copy the map, and then add more links to your map. Also, you may add more information in each box.

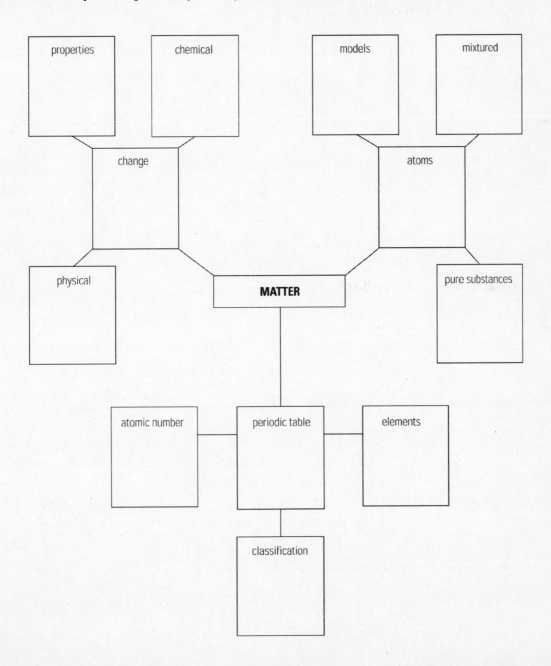

A concept map can be used to review a large topic on a general level, or it can be used to examine a very specific topic in detail. Select one concept from this unit that you need to study more, and make a detailed concept map for it in the space below.

 *Challenge*

Once you have chosen your Challenge, use the space that follows to answer the Challenge questions from your text. You may also want to use these pages to record any ideas or to draw tables, graphs, or sketches that relate to your Challenge.

Challenge	Section and page in textbook	
1 Marketing Matter	Section 1.1, page 13 Section 1.2, page 14 Section 1.3, page 17 Section 1.4, page 19 Section 1.6, page 23 Section 1.8, page 27 Section 1.9, page 31 Section 1.11, page 35	Section 1.12, page 37 Section 1.14, page 41 Section 1.19, page 51 Section 1.20, page 54
2 Time Capsule	Section 1.1, page 13 Section 1.2, page 14 Section 1.3, page 17 Section 1.4, page 19 Section 1.5, page 21 Section 1.6, page 23 Section 1.8, page 27 Section 1.10, page 33 Section 1.11, page 35 Section 1.13, page 39 Section 1.16, page 45	Section 1.19, page 51 Section 1.20, page 54
3 A Famous Scientist	Section 1.3, page 17 Section 1.6, page 23 Section 1.8, page 27 Section 1.9, page 31 Section 1.10, page 33 Section 1.11, page 35 Section 1.12, page 37 Section 1.13, page 39 Section 1.18, page 49	

Challenge Journal

_____

_____

_____

_____

_____

_____

_____

_____

_____

_____

_____

_____

_____

_____

_____

_____

_____

_____

_____

_____

 *Challenge*

Reproduction and Reproductive Technology

As you learn about cell division and reproduction, you will be able to explain how this knowledge is important to humans. You will also be able to demonstrate your learning by completing one of the following Challenges.

1 Reproductive Technology

Choose a reproductive technology and prepare a report in pamphlet form that will inform the general public about the issues and the advantages and disadvantages of the technology.

2 Plant Experiment

Plan and conduct an experiment to investigate factors that affect the growth and development of plants, and report the results of your investigation.

3 Analyzing Cancer Risk

Design an instrument or rating scale that will help people analyze their cancer risk, and make recommendations that will help people lower their risk of cancer.

Choose a Challenge. Use the space on pages 196–198 to answer the Challenge questions from your text and to record your ideas for your challenge.

How I Am Being Assessed _____

_____

1. Do all cells look alike? Explain.

   _____

   _____

   _____

   _____

   _____

2. Explain the similarities and differences between plant and animal cells. Use sketches in your explanation.

   _____

   _____

   _____

   _____

   _____

   _____

Plant cell	Animal cell

3. Why is it important for cells to divide rather than to simply grow larger?

_____

_____

_____

_____

4. Where in the cell is genetic information found? What is the purpose of this genetic information?

_____

_____

_____

_____

5. (a) Give two examples of different methods of reproduction in plants.

_____

_____

_____

_____

(b) Do all animals reproduce in the same way? Explain.

_____

_____

_____

_____

_____

Think back to what you learned in earlier grades.

Use the following terms to label the parts of the animal cell below:

cell membrane   mitochondrion
nucleus   cytoplasm
endoplasmic reticulum   vacuole
Golgi apparatus

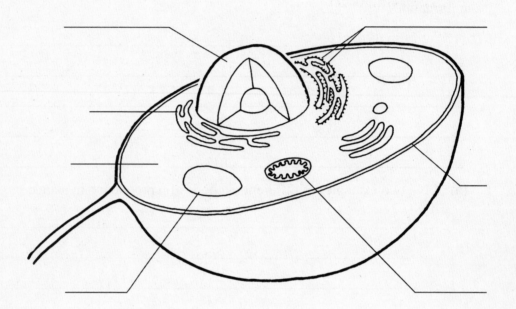

How I Am Being Assessed _____

_____

Cell Replacement

(a) Predict from which area the stain will first disappear.

_____

_____

_____

_____

_____

Observe the stained areas daily and record your observations.

Day	Palm of hand	Back of hand
1		
2		
3		
4		
5		
6		
7		

(b) Explain your observations.

_____

_____

_____

_____

How I Am Being Assessed _____

_____

Limits on Cell Size

Examine the agar cubes, then answer the following:

(a) Describe the appearance of each cube.

_____

_____

_____

(b) If the nucleus (control centre) is located in the middle of each cube, how quickly will each cube react to changes in the environment?

_____

_____

(c) If the coloured part of the cell receives food and gets rid of wastes, which cell would do a better job of carrying out these functions? Explain why.

_____

_____

_____

(d) Why are large animals made up of many cells and not just one giant cell?

_____

_____

_____

_____

_____

How I Am Being Assessed _____

_____

Understanding Concepts

1. How are plant and animal cells alike?

   _____

   _____

2. What differences do you notice between plant and animal cells, from **Figure 1** on page 70 of your text?

   _____

   _____

3. Give three reasons cells divide.

   _____

   _____

   _____

4. Draw a large cell and a small cell. Label the nucleus, cytoplasm, and cell membrane. Show the directions in which food and wastes travel.

Refer to your diagrams and explain why a small cell works better than a large cell.

_____

_____

_____

_____

Making Connections

5. In the early 1900s, doctors gave elderly patients blood transfusions from younger people. The doctors believed that the younger blood would give the elderly people more energy. Do older people actually have older blood? Support your answer. (Hint: Use information from Did You Know? page 71 in your text.)

_____

_____

_____

_____

Can you answer this bonus question?

As you have learned in this section, cells divide for three reasons: healing and tissue repair, growth, and reproduction of organisms. Read each of the following statements and decide which reason it best describes. Write the answer on the line provided.

(a) Cells form along a crack in a bone that was broken in a skiing accident.

_____

(b) A starfish loses a limb to a predator, and a new limb grows in.

_____

(c) New yeast cells form buds off mother cells inside a bowl of rising bread dough.

_____

(d) A tomato increases in size over 50 days before it is ready to harvest.

_____

(e) Male fish produce sperm and release them directly onto egg clusters laid by female fish.

_____

(f) A red blood cell becomes too old to function well; a new red blood cell is made in the liver.

_____

(g) A small spider plant grows larger and then produces runners with little spiders at the end.

_____

How I Am Being Assessed _____

_____

Doing the Chromosome Shuffle!

In this investigation, you will model the cell cycle by acting out the process of cell division.

Question

What happens inside the nucleus when a cell divides?

Materials

Your teacher will provide the following materials:
- 6 cardboard chromosomes (3 pairs of different colours)
- cell component name cards (cell membrane, nuclear membrane, chromosome)

Procedure

1. You will play the roles of the various cell components. For example, 10 students will be the cell membrane (holding hands in a circle), another 8 students will be the nuclear membrane, and 6 students will be the chromosomes. (Adjust the numbers so that all students are involved.)

2. At the beginning, set up the cell during **interphase**. During this phase, the cell grows and prepares for division by duplicating its genetic material. Start with 10 students for the cell membrane. As the cell grows, add any additional students. At the beginning, three student chromosomes (holding cardboard cut-out chromosomes) will all be bunched together inside the nucleus (**Figure 1**). During duplication, add another student chromosome to each to form a pair of identical chromosomes. The nucleus now has six chromosomes (three double-stranded chromosomes).

Figure 1

3. During **prophase**, the chromosomes shorten and thicken and the nuclear membrane starts to dissolve. Have students act out these processes, maybe by crouching down and becoming as short as possible. The students who are holding hands to form the nuclear membrane will begin to loosen their hold and, one by one, gradually leave the cell circle.

4. During **metaphase**, the double-stranded chromosomes line up across the middle of the cell. Students should shuffle into their positions, taking very small steps (**Figure 2**).

5. During **anaphase**, the chromosome strands separate, with one strand going to each end of the cell.

Figure 2

6. In **telophase**, the chromosomes reach the opposite ends of the cell and a new nuclear membrane starts to form around each set. The students who represent the nuclear membrane will reenter the cell. Half of them will go to each end and start to hold hands around the sets of chromosomes.

7. **Cytokinesis** starts, and the cell membrane starts to form around each nucleus. The cell membrane students must pinch the circle in half and eventually form two separate cell membranes.

8. At this point, the two daughter cells are in interphase and the process of growth begins.

9. Repeat the steps until the group can demonstrate a smooth cell division. If possible, do the "chromosome shuffle" in the gymnasium and videotape the process from a point above the floor.

Observations

Record your observations and your feelings about the activity.

_____

_____

_____

_____

_____

_____

_____

_____

_____

Analysis and Conclusion

(a) Explain what happens in the nucleus during mitosis.

_____

_____

_____

_____

_____

(b) Is this a good model of cell division? Explain why or why not.

_____

_____

_____

_____

_____

(c) Which phase of mitosis was most difficult to demonstrate? Explain why.

_____

_____

_____

_____

_____

(d) Suggest another way of demonstrating the processes of cell division.

_____

_____

_____

_____

_____

2.2 Cell Division

Questions

How I Am Being Assessed _____

_____

Understanding Concepts

1. Describe the cell cycle. What happens during interphase?

   _____

   _____

   _____

   _____

   _____

2. Why is it necessary to duplicate the nuclear material?

   _____

   _____

   _____

3. List and describe the four phases of mitosis.

   _____

   _____

   _____

   _____

   _____

   _____

4. A normal human cell has 46 chromosomes. After the cell has undergone mitosis, how many chromosomes would you expect to find in each daughter cell? Explain.

   _____

   _____

Making Connections

5. X-rays and other forms of radiation can break chromosomes apart. Doctors and dentists ask women whether they are pregnant before taking X-rays. Why don't they want to X-ray pregnant women?

_____

_____

Reflecting

6. Sketch an outline of a human body. On the sketch, identify the areas of the body where you think cell division is most rapid. Why do you think cells from these areas divide most rapidly?

Work the Web

Do all cells divide at the same rate? Explain.

_____

_____

_____

_____

2.3 Activity

Observing Cell Division

Report

How I Am Being Assessed _____

_____

(a) How can you tell whether the cells are dividing?

_____

_____

_____

_____

Onion Root Tip

(b) Draw and label each of the phases that you see. Label chromosomes if they are visible. It is important to draw and label only the structures that you see under the microscope.

Phase:_____	Phase:_____
Phase:_____	Phase:_____

Whitefish Embryo

(c) Draw and give a title to each of the phases that you see. Label the chromosomes if they are visible.

Phase:_____	Phase:_____
Phase:_____	Phase:_____

2.3 Activity
Observing Cell Division

Questions

How I Am Being Assessed _____

_____

Understanding Concepts

1. Why were plant root tip cells and animal embryo cells used for viewing cell division?

   _____

   _____

   _____

2. Explain why the cells that you viewed under the microscope do not continue to divide.

   _____

   _____

   _____

3. Use a table to list the differences and similarities between the appearance of the dividing animal cells and the dividing plant cells.

Differences between dividing animal cells and dividing plant cells	**Similarities** between dividing animal cells and dividing plant cells

4. If a cell has 10 chromosomes, how many chromosomes will each cell have following cell division by mitosis? Explain.

   _____

   _____

5. Predict what might happen to each daughter cell if all the chromosomes moved to only one side of the cell during anaphase.

_____

_____

_____

Exploring

6. Search the Internet for pictures of plant and animal cells that are dividing. How closely did your microscope observations resemble these pictures? Explain any differences.

_____

_____

_____

_____

_____

7. In this investigation, you observed cells in various phases of cell division. Did you observe any cells that did not appear normal? What might have gone wrong with these cells.

_____

_____

_____

_____

Work the Web

What proportion of cells is undergoing mitosis at any point in time? Explain.

_____

_____

_____

_____

_____

_____

2.3 Activity: Observing Cell Division **117**

2.4 Case Study
Cell Division and Growth

Report

How I Am Being Assessed _____

_____

(a) Which parts of the body appear to grow the most between a two-month-old fetus and an infant?

_____

_____

(b) Which parts of the body appear to grow the most between infancy and adulthood?

_____

_____

(c) Which parts of the body grow the least during each time period in (a) and (b)?

_____

_____

(d) Why do you think an infant's head is so large compared with the rest of its body?

_____

_____

_____

(e) By how many times has the body mass increased by age 20? By how many times has the heart mass increased in the same period?

_____

_____

(f) At what approximate age does the brain reach its maximum mass?

_____

_____

(g) How does the growth of the heart compare with that of the brain?

_____

_____

_____

(h) Would you expect the increase in the mass of the heart and the body to continue at the same rate after 20 years of age? Explain your answer.

_____

_____

_____

(i) Which grows faster, the foot or the shin bone?

_____

_____

(j) Describe what would happen if the bones in the feet grew at the same rate as the tibia.

_____

_____

_____

2.4 Case Study Cell Division and Growth — *Questions*

How I Am Being Assessed ____________________

____

Understanding Concepts

1. Where in your body would you expect to see the highest rate of cell division? Explain your answer.

2. Based on the information in **Figure 2** (page 77 of your text, and Figure 2 on the next page), what can you conclude about the growth of your brain?

Applying Skills

3. An experiment measured the rate of growth of a seedling root. Lines were marked on the root 1 mm apart. After 48 h, the root appeared as shown below. Draw a conclusion based on these results.

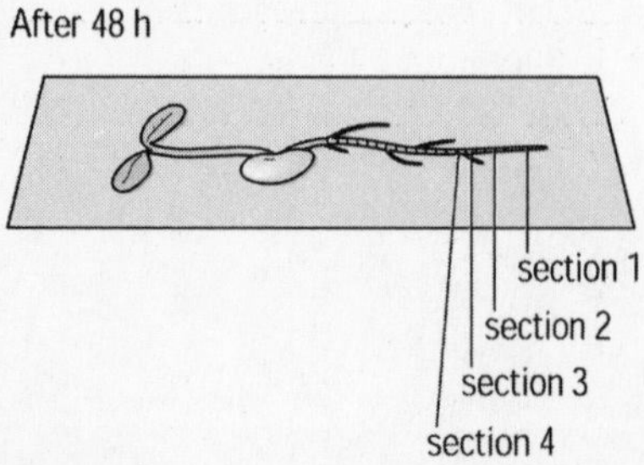
After 48 h
section 1
section 2
section 3
section 4

Figure 1

Making Connections

4. The graph of the growth rates in **Figure 2** from page 77 of your textbook is taken from data collected from a large group of people. Why do scientists obtain data from many people rather than from a single person?

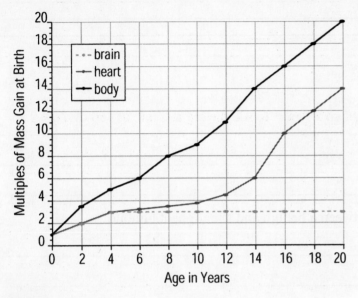

Figure 2
Growth rates of the brain, heart, and body

Reflecting

5. What evidence do you have from your own growth patterns that suggests that all parts of your body do not grow at the same rate? If possible, use photographs of yourself at different ages as evidence.

_____

_____

_____

_____

_____

_____

2.5 Cancer

Questions

How I Am Being Assessed _____

_____

Understanding Concepts

1. What is a mutation?

   _____

   _____

   _____

2. Explain the difference between a benign and a malignant tumour.

   _____

   _____

   _____

   _____

3. What is cancer?

   _____

   _____

   _____

4. In what ways are cancer cells different from normal cells?

   _____

   _____

   _____

   _____

Making Connections

5. Not all rapid cell growth is cancerous. A certain virus causes skin cells to divide quickly, producing a wart. Imagine what would happen if a cell and its descendants divided every hour. Fill in the blanks in the table below. Explain the pattern you observe in the number of cells.

Time (h)	Number of cells
0	1
1	2
2	4
3	
4	
5	
6	

_____

_____

_____

_____

6. Choose one type of cancer and prepare a brief summary that considers the following points:
   - What causes this type of cancer (e.g., virus, chemicals, radiation, unknown)?
   - What treatments are available?
   - How dangerous is the cancer?

_____

_____

_____

_____

_____

_____

_____

_____

_____

_____

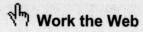 **Work the Web**

Cancers may be linked to certain environmental conditions.

What kinds of environmental conditions are linked to cancer?

_____

_____

_____

_____

What types of cancer are most commonly linked to each environmental cause?

_____

_____

_____

2.6 Activity
Lifestyle and Cancer
Report

How I Am Being Assessed _____

_____

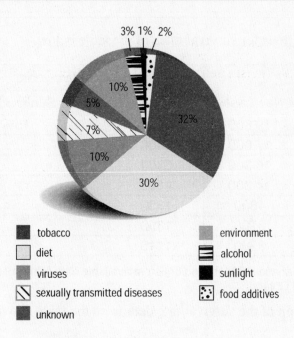

Figure 1
Estimates of cancer risk factors

Legend:
- tobacco
- diet
- viruses
- sexually transmitted diseases
- unknown
- environment
- alcohol
- sunlight
- food additives

(a) Which factor is responsible for most cancer cases?

_____

_____

_____

(b) Which of the cancer causes could be reduced by changes in lifestyle?

_____

_____

_____

(c) List three lifestyle changes that could reduce cancer rates.

_____

_____

_____

_____

_____

_____

Complete the calculations for survival rates in the table below.

Type of cancer	New cases	After five years	
		Deaths	Survival rate
lung	19 600	16 600	15%
breast	17 000	5400	
colon	16 300	6300	
prostate	14 300	4100	
bladder	4800	1350	
kidney	3700	1350	
leukemia	3200	1110	

Source: Statistics Canada, 1994, based on latest available data from British Columbia, Saskatchewan, and Ontario.

(d) Draw a bar graph of the survival rate data from the table above.

Cancer Five-Year Survival Rate

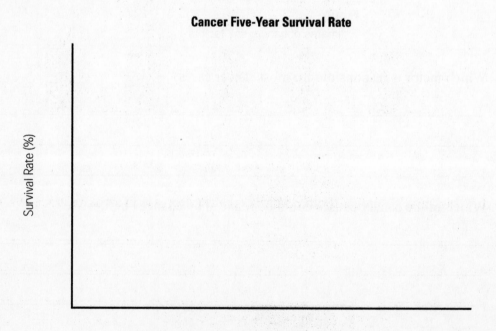

Survival Rate (%)

Type of Cancer

(e) How do you think these estimates of survival rates were obtained?

_____

_____

_____

(f) Based on these data, which type of cancer is most deadly? Which type has the best survival rate?

_____

_____

_____

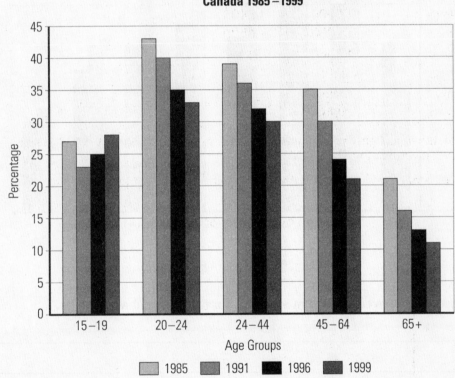

**Smokers as Percentage of Total Population
Canada 1985–1999**

(g) In which age group has there been the greatest decrease in smokers since 1985?

_____

_____

_____

(h) Based on your experience, suggest a possible explanation for the data for the 15–19 age group.

_____

_____

_____

_____

_____

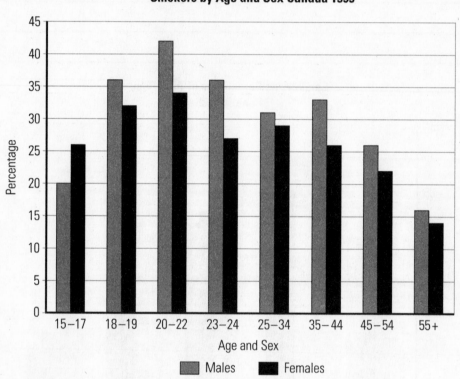

Smokers by Age and Sex Canada 1999

(i) Describe the overall trend in smoking for the different age groups.

_____

_____

_____

_____

_____

_____

(j) Describe the differences between the sexes.

_____

_____

_____

_____

(k) Propose a possible explanation for the differences between the sexes in the 15–17 age group.

_____

_____

_____

_____

_____

How I Am Being Assessed _____

_____

Understanding Concepts

1. What is a carcinogen? Give three examples.

   _____

   _____

   _____

   _____

   _____

2. The chemicals in the tar from cigarette smoke are known to cause cancer. Calculate the amount of tar absorbed by a smoker in one week. The following information will help you with your calculations:
   • Assume that a smoker smokes 10 cigarettes a day.
   • There are 20 mg of tar in most cigarettes (1000 mg = 1 g).
   • Approximately 25% of the tar is released in the form of smoke or is exhaled. The remaining 75% is absorbed through the smoker's lungs.

   _____

   _____

   _____

   _____

   _____

Exploring

3. The money spent on cancer treatment continues to grow every year. One politician has suggested that cancers caused by smoking should be given a lower priority for treatment. Explain why you agree or disagree with this suggestion.

   _____

   _____

   _____

_____

_____

_____

_____

_____

Reflecting

4. What changes could you make in your lifestyle that would reduce your cancer risk? Will these changes be easy? Explain.

_____

_____

_____

_____

_____

_____

_____

_____

✍ Work the Web

Diet is the second-highest risk factor for cancer. Find information to determine what features of our diet are responsible for the higher risk of cancer.

_____

_____

_____

_____

_____

_____

_____

_____

How I Am Being Assessed _____

_____

Should we be fighting nature?

What Do You Think?

Which side of the debate have you been assigned to?

_____

_____

In your group, discuss the statement and the points and counterpoints. Record additional points and counterpoints that your group considers.

Statement Hormones or drugs should not be used to stop or slow down the processes of aging.	
Point	**Counterpoint**
• The idea of reversing aging presents many difficulties. First, the cost would be immense. Hormone treatment is expensive. At current prices, injections for a 70-kg man would cost about $14 000 per year. Only the richest people would be able to pay for such treatments. • Extending the lifespan of the average person might cause overpopulation of Earth. There might not be enough food to support the increased population. The cost of caring for elderly people would increase.	• Expense has no bearing on the issue. If people spend billions of dollars on cosmetics, then they'll spend money on hormones or other treatments. • The money spent on hormones or other treatments would produce economic benefits. For example, people would work longer and generally experience a better quality of life. • Overpopulation can be avoided using various methods of family planning. Food supplies could be increased by advances in science and technology. Health costs would decrease because elderly people would be healthier.

Search newspapers, a library periodical index, a CD-ROM directory, and the Internet for information on drugs or hormones used to slow aging.

_____

_____

_____

_____

_____

_____

_____

Prepare to defend your group's position in a class debate.

Spokesperson(s) _____

_____

_____

_____

_____

_____

_____

_____

2.7 Explore an Issue
Search for the Fountain of Youth

Questions

How I Am Being Assessed _____

_____

Understanding the Issue

1. Which age groups will increase and which age groups will decrease in Canada's future population?

   _____

   _____

   _____

   _____

   _____

2. Which anti-aging approach do you think might be easiest to achieve? Explain.

   _____

   _____

   _____

   _____

   _____

3. If the average life expectancy in Canada is 79 years, does this mean that everyone will live to be 79 years old? Explain.

   _____

   _____

   _____

   _____

   _____

How I Am Being Assessed _____

_____

Complete the graphic organizer below to summarize the key concepts presented to this point.

Write a statement for each arrow to explain the connections between the words or phrases.

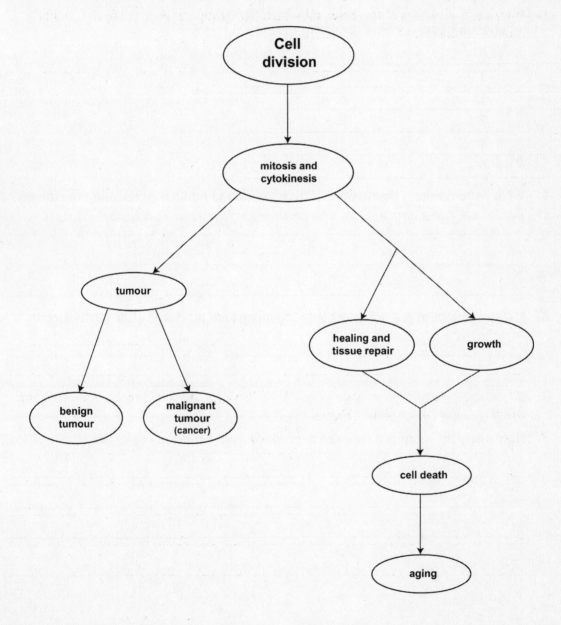

2.8 Cell Division and Reproduction

How I Am Being Assessed _____

_____

How Many Divisions Will It Take?

Complete the table below.

Number of divisions	Number of organisms
0	1
1	2
2	4
3	
4	
5	

1. What pattern relates the number of divisions to the number of resulting organisms?

   _____

   _____

   _____

2. Use the pattern to predict how many organisms are produced after 10 divisions.

   _____

   _____

   _____

3. How many divisions are required to produce over 1 million organisms?

   _____

   _____

   _____

4. The single, fertilized cell from which you began divided to produce the many cells that make up your body. Estimate how many cell divisions it took. (Assume that there are a trillion cells in your body. A trillion is 1 000 000 000 000.)

_____

_____

_____

Bonus Question

The graph below shows the growth of a population of an organism that reproduces asexually, if all the organisms survive and continue to divide.

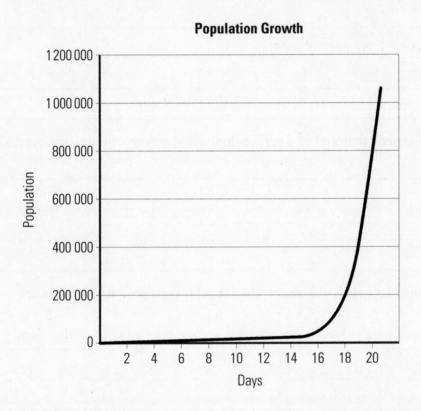

Population Growth

Is this the pattern you would expect from a real population? Explain why or why not.

_____

_____

_____

_____

_____

How I Am Being Assessed _____

_____

Understanding Concepts

1. How is asexual reproduction different from sexual reproduction?

   _____

   _____

   _____

   _____

2. Why must the genetic material of a cell be duplicated before cell division begins?

   _____

   _____

   _____

   _____

3. What is a zygote? How is it different from daughter cells produced by asexual reproduction?

   _____

   _____

   _____

   _____

4. What is the main advantage of sexual reproduction?

   _____

   _____

   _____

   _____

5. **(a)** Briefly describe the five types of asexual reproduction.

_____

_____

_____

_____

_____

(b) Choose one type of asexual reproduction. Explain how a plant nursery could make use of it.

_____

_____

_____

_____

6. Starfish feed on mussels and other shellfish. Operators of mussel farms have been known to cut up starfish and throw them overboard. Is this a smart practice? Explain.

_____

_____

_____

_____

7. Identify the method of asexual reproduction in each of the following situations:

(a) A multicellular algae is struck by a wave. The algae breaks up and each new piece grows into a new organism.

_____

_____

(b) A new tree begins to grow from the root of a nearby tree.

_____

_____

(c) A small cell begins to grow on the outside of another cell. Eventually, it breaks away from the larger cell and continues to grow.

_____

_____

8. Why is DNA fingerprinting a useful tool in criminal investigations?

_____

_____

_____

_____

Reflecting

9. What advantages might an organism that can reproduce asexually have? Make a list of the advantages. Add to your list or modify it as you progress through this unit.

_____

_____

_____

_____

_____

Exploring

10. Describe what happens during each of the two cell divisions that produce sex cells.

_____

_____

_____

_____

_____

_____

_____

_____

Work the Web

Briefly describe the process of DNA fingerprinting.

_____

_____

_____

_____

_____

_____

_____

Report on a criminal case that used DNA fingerprinting as evidence.

_____

_____

_____

_____

_____

_____

_____

How I Am Being Assessed _____

_____

Understanding Concepts

1. What is cloning?

   _____

   _____

   _____

   _____

2. In what ways are plants cloned?

   _____

   _____

   _____

   _____

3. Explain why cloning is considered asexual reproduction.

   _____

   _____

   _____

   _____

4. Dolly was not the first cloned animal or the first cloned mammal. What made her cloning so special?

   _____

   _____

   _____

   _____

Making Connections

5. Imagine that farmers were able to easily clone any animal in their herd or flock. What might be the benefits for food production? Would there be any disadvantages? Explain.

_____

_____

_____

_____

_____

_____

_____

_____

_____

Reflecting

6. What ethical issues can you list that relate to cloning? Write a paragraph sharing your views on one of these issues.

_____

_____

_____

_____

_____

_____

_____

_____

_____

_____

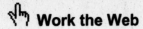 **Work the Web**

There is much debate about whether humans should be cloned.

Identify two countries that have banned human cloning research, and describe the measures and reasons for banning this research.

_____

_____

_____

_____

_____

_____

_____

Identify two countries that are funding or supporting human cloning research. What are their arguments?

_____

_____

_____

_____

_____

_____

_____

What is Canada's position on human cloning research?

_____

_____

_____

_____

_____

2.10 Investigation
Cloning from Plant Cuttings

Report

How I Am Being Assessed _____

_____

In this investigation, you will grow a plant from a cutting, thereby making a clone of the original plant.

Question

What is the process for cloning plants?

Prediction

(a) Write a prediction for this investigation.

_____

_____

Observations

(b) Record your observations daily.

Day	Observations
1	
2	
3	
4	
5	
6	
7	
8	
9	
10	
11	
12	
13	
14	

(c) In the table below, record the growth of each plant for three weeks after transplanting.

Day	Height of plant	Comments
0		
2		
4		
6		
8		
10		
12		
14		
16		
18		
20		
22		

(d) Observe the pots every other day for several weeks, and record your observations in the table below.

Day/Date	Height of plant	Comments
0		
2		
4		
6		
8		
10		
12		
14		
16		
18		
20		
22		
24		
26		
28		
30		
32		
34		
36		
38		
40		
42		
44		
46		

Analysis and Conclusion

(e) What evidence suggests that coleus has the ability to regenerate parts of the plant lost to injury?

_____

_____

_____

(f) In what ways would the new coleus resemble the parent plant?

_____

_____

_____

(g) Suggest two ways to prove that the roots from the coleus cuttings are growing.

_____

_____

_____

_____

(h) If you continue growing a potato plant, would you expect to get more than one new potato? Explain.

_____

_____

_____

(i) Was your prediction for this investigation correct? Explain why or why not, based on your observations.

_____

_____

_____

(j) Based on your observations, what is present in the eye of the potato?

_____

_____

_____

2.10 Investigation
Cloning from Plant Cuttings
Questions

How I Am Being Assessed _____

_____

Understanding Concepts

1. A hailstorm can shred most plants. After a hailstorm, what advantage would a coleus plant have over plants that cannot reproduce vegetatively?

_____

_____

_____

_____

2. Explain the advantage of growing potatoes from tuber cuttings.

_____

_____

_____

3. Explain why you should keep the leaves of the coleus cuttings out of the water.

_____

_____

_____

Exploring

4. Plan and carry out an investigation to determine whether the size of the piece of cutting is a factor in cloning potatoes. Or, find out whether you can grow a coleus from a single leaf.

_____

_____

_____

_____

_____

_____

_____

5. Grow a pineapple clone using the method shown in **Figure 1**. Record your observations.

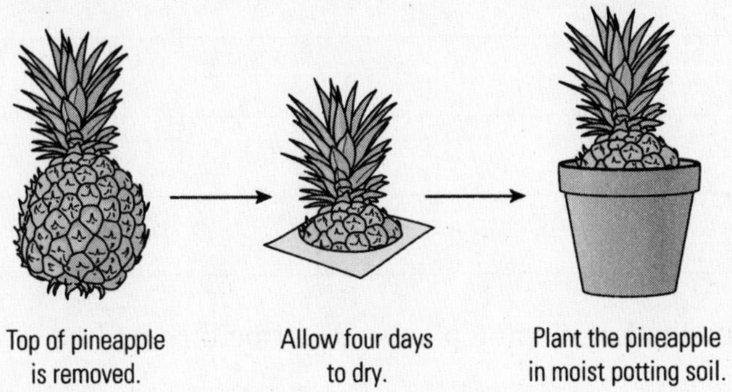

Top of pineapple is removed.   Allow four days to dry.   Plant the pineapple in moist potting soil.

Figure 1

_____

_____

_____

_____

_____

_____

_____

_____

_____

_____

_____

_____

_____

_____

Work the Web

Research to find other plants that can be easily cloned by vegetative reproduction.

_____

_____

_____

_____

_____

Grafting is another common method of cloning plants. Describe this method.

_____

_____

_____

_____

_____

2.11 Sexual Reproduction

Extension Activity

How I Am Being Assessed _____

_____

Simulating Sexual Reproduction

In sexual reproduction, two sex cells combine to form a zygote. There is more than one way this can happen.

In this simulation, a plastic bag represents an organism, and coloured licorice represents male and female sex cells. For sexual reproduction to occur, somehow the genetic information from the two organisms must mix.

- Work with a partner.
- Take two small self-locking bags. One contains four pieces of black licorice; the other contains four pieces of red licorice.
- Find four different ways to mix the genetic information (licorice) in these bags. You may remove the licorice to do the mixing.

(a) Draw diagrams to represent different ways of combining the genetic information.

Possibility 1	Possibility 2
Possibility 3	Possibility 4

(b) Which diagram(s) represent(s) internal fertilization? _____

(c) Which diagram(s) represent(s) external fertilization? _____

(d) Which diagram(s) represent(s) hermaphrodism? _____

(e) Which diagram(s) represent(s) conjugation? _____

(f) Which diagram(s) represent(s) separate sexes? _____

Copyright © 2003 Nelson

2.11 Sexual Reproduction **151**

| How I Am Being Assessed _____ |
| _____ |

Understanding Concepts

1. Describe how conjugation is different from human reproduction.

2. How many chromosomes do the cells in **Figure 2** on page 92 of your text have?

   (a) egg _____

   (b) sperm _____

   (c) zygote _____

3. How are the chromosomes in a female zygote different from those in a male zygote?

   _____

   _____

4. Using keywords (sex cells, egg, sperm, fertilization, zygote), explain how external and internal fertilization are the same and how they are different.

   _____

   _____

   _____

   _____

   _____

5. What makes an earthworm a hermaphrodite, and how does this help it reproduce?

   _____

   _____

   _____

   _____

6. How is a plant a hermaphrodite? Use the information in **Figure 4** on page 93 of your text to answer this question.

_____

_____

_____

Making Connections

7. List as many differences as you can between sexual and asexual reproduction, using information presented in the sections so far.

Sexual reproduction	Asexual reproduction

Can you answer this bonus question?

Frogs reproduce through external fertilization. Use the Internet or library resources to describe how this occurs.

_____

_____

_____

_____

_____

_____

_____

How I Am Being Assessed _____

_____

In this investigation, you will examine different flowers to see which structures they have in common and which are different. You will also look at the functions of the parts of a flower.

Question

How do flowers differ from one another?

Prediction

(a) Create a prediction for this question.

_____

Observations

Follow the procedure instructions and record all information in this table.

Table 1: **Flower Comparison**

Characteristic	Flower 1	Flower 2
number of petals		
number of sepals		
number of stamens		
number of pistils		
labelled diagram of flower (remember to identify female and male structures)		
labelled diagram of pistil		

Analysis and Conclusion

(b) Was your prediction correct? Explain why or why not, based on your observations.

_____

_____

_____

_____

(c) List the ways in which the two flowers were similar. Why would this be the case?

_____

_____

_____

_____

_____

_____

(d) List the ways in which the two flowers were different. Why would this be the case? (Hint: Consider how the flower is pollinated and how its seeds are dispersed.)

_____

_____

_____

_____

_____

_____

(e) Were any of the parts in **Figure 1** on page 94 of your text missing in your flowers? Describe any differences.

_____

_____

_____

_____

How I Am Being Assessed _____

_____

Understanding Concepts

1. What happens when the pollen reaches the egg? What do the fertilized eggs become?

   _____

   _____

2. In what part of the flower do seeds form?

   _____

3. How do insects and birds help with the process of pollination?

   _____

   _____

   _____

   _____

Exploring

4. Hummingbirds are attracted to red trumpet-shaped flowers. They hover over the flowers and use their long beak to collect nectar. In this way, the flowers are pollinated. Using the Internet or other resources, find two other examples of how flowers and animals have developed special structures to ensure pollination.

   _____

   _____

   _____

   _____

   _____

   _____

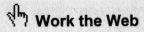 **Work the Web**

Hay fever is the name given to pollen allergies. One in eight Canadian students has asthma, which can be triggered by pollen allergies. Find out more about hay fever. Answer these questions: what? who? when? where? why? and discuss available treatments.

_____

_____

_____

_____

_____

_____

_____

_____

_____

_____

_____

_____

_____

_____

_____

_____

_____

How I Am Being Assessed _____

_____

(a) What percentage of Earth's landmass is used for cropland? Why is this the case?

_____

_____

_____

(b) Use the table below to summarize the traditional methods of increasing food production. Define and give two examples of each method.

Traditional method	Definition	Examples
selective breeding		
cloning		
grafting		

(c) Study **Figure 3** on page 96 of your text. What are two advantages and two disadvantages of this grafting method?

_____

_____

_____

_____

(d) List three ways in which genetic engineering has improved crops.

_____

_____

_____

_____

_____

(e) What disadvantages of genetic engineering can you think of?

_____

_____

_____

_____

_____

(f) How did Canadian scientists modify rapeseed to make it more pleasing to the consumer?

_____

_____

_____

(g) Compare traditional breeding methods and genetic engineering methods using this table. List three strengths and three weaknesses of each method.

Agricultural method	Strengths	Weaknesses
traditional breeding		
genetic engineering		

2.13 Case Study
Reproduction of Plants for Food

How I Am Being Assessed _____

_____

Simulated Gene Splicing

Follow the procedure on page 97 of your text, and answer the following questions:

(a) Why was the jar relabelled in the last step?

_____

_____

(b) Jar A no longer represents a complete nucleus. Explain why.

_____

_____

(c) Summarize this activity in a labelled diagram.

(d) Make up an example to accompany this activity. For example, what plant is being modified? What does the red segment contain, and what species does it come from? How is the new plant different from the original? What will happen when the new plant reproduces?

_____

_____

_____

_____

_____

2.13 Case Study

Reproduction of Plants for Food

How I Am Being Assessed _____

_____

Understanding Concepts

1. Why is it so important to increase food production?

   _____

   _____

   _____

   _____

2. How do selective breeding, cloning, and grafting increase food production?

   _____

   _____

   _____

   _____

3. List three ways in which genetic engineering of plant crops could increase food production.

   _____

   _____

   _____

   _____

Reflecting

4. What is your personal opinion of GM foods? Write a paragraph that includes some of the information presented in this case study. Remember to write an introduction and a conclusion.

_____

_____

_____

_____

_____

_____

_____

_____

_____

Work the Web

Find out more about a specific food that has been changed using selective breeding or genetic engineering. (Examples of genetically engineered foods include corn, wheat, canola, McIntosh apples, tastier tomatoes, and seedless watermelons.) What improvements were made, and how were they done?

_____

_____

_____

_____

_____

_____

_____

_____

How I Am Being Assessed _____

_____

Understanding Concepts

1. Use a dictionary to find the most appropriate definitions for new terms in this section.

   (a) arborist

   _____

   _____

   (b) fertility

   _____

   _____

   (c) fungicide

   _____

   _____

   (d) herbicide

   _____

   _____

   (e) horticulturist

   _____

   _____

   (f) insecticide

   _____

   _____

   (g) perennial

   _____

   _____

Making Connections

2. Review section 2.10, and explain what you think is meant by "soft- and hardwood cuttings."

_____

_____

_____

3. What interests and skills would you need to succeed as a horticulturist?

_____

_____

_____

_____

Work the Web

Find out more about careers in agriculture across Canada. What diploma courses in horticulture are available? List other opportunities in agriculture that do not require a university degree.

_____

_____

_____

_____

_____

_____

_____

_____

How I Am Being Assessed _____

_____

Observing Human Variation

Do you look like your brother or sister? Do you and your friends resemble one another? You will likely find more similarities with your family members and fewer similarities with your friends. Physical traits are passed on through genes.

In this activity, you will compare physical traits displayed by you and other students.

- Review the traits in **Figure 1**.

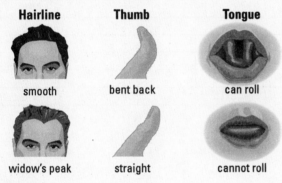

Figure 1
Three common physical traits

In **Table 1**, use a check mark to record which traits each class member has.

Table 1 Comparison of Traits

Characteristic	Hairline		Thumb		Tongue	
traits	smooth	widow's peak	bent back	straight	Can roll	Cannot roll
student 1						
student 2						

- Design a bar graph to plot the results.

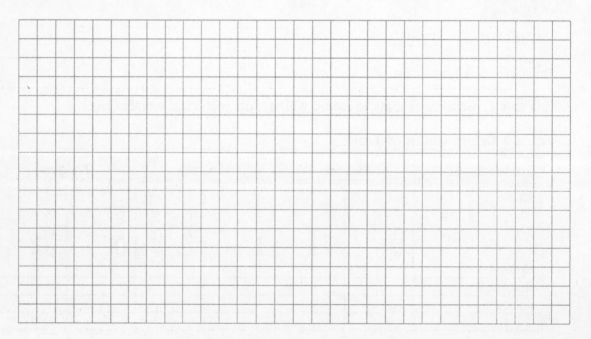

Use your table and graph to answer the following:

(a) Which form of each trait is most common?

_____

_____

_____

_____

(b) Express the class data for each trait using a ratio. (Example: If there are 12 males in the class and 9 females, the male:female ratio is 12:9, or 4:3.)

_____

_____

_____

_____

(c) Why do you think your classmates do not all have the same traits?

_____

_____

_____

(d) Choose one of the above traits. Compare four family members for this trait. Do you see a pattern? If so, suggest a possible explanation for it.

_____

_____

_____

(e) Name three other traits that are passed on through genes.

_____

_____

_____

How I Am Being Assessed	_____
	_____

Understanding Concepts

1. Use the table below to compare and contrast asexual and sexual reproduction. Summarize information from previous sections as well.

Comparison	Asexual reproduction	Sexual reproduction
similarities		
differences		

2. Classify the following as either sexual or asexual reproduction:

   (a) A small piece of a cactus breaks off the plant, falls to the ground, and begins to grow. _____

   (b) Pollen from a male poplar tree fertilizes sex cells on a female poplar tree

   _____

   (c) Two earthworms each produce sperm and eggs and fertilize each other. Eggs are laid. _____

   (d) A flatworm is cut in half and grows into two flatworms. _____

   Add three examples of your own.

   (e) _____

   _____

   (f) _____

   _____

(g) _____

_____

3. How can two sisters with the same parents have different hair colours?

_____

_____

_____

4. Identify an organism that uses each of the following strategies to make sure its offspring survive. Describe the strategy more fully, and explain why it is used.

(a) The zygote is wrapped in a food package.

_____

_____

_____

(b) This package can be fertilized externally or internally.

_____

_____

_____

(c) The young develop within the adult organism.

_____

_____

_____

(d) Under unfavourable conditions, the zygote remains inactive.

_____

_____

_____

Making Connections

5. Consider the place of bacteria on the concept map (**Figure 1** on page 100 of your text). They can reproduce both asexually and sexually. Describe each method they use. What advantage is gained by using both methods?

_____

_____

_____

_____

_____

_____

_____

_____

_____

6. If the entire planet became tropical through climate change, which survival strategy presented here would best ensure the survival of humans? Explain your answer.

_____

_____

_____

_____

_____

_____

_____

How I Am Being Assessed _____

_____

Complete the graphic organizer below to summarize the key concepts presented to this point.

Define each word and include an example of an organism that uses this strategy.

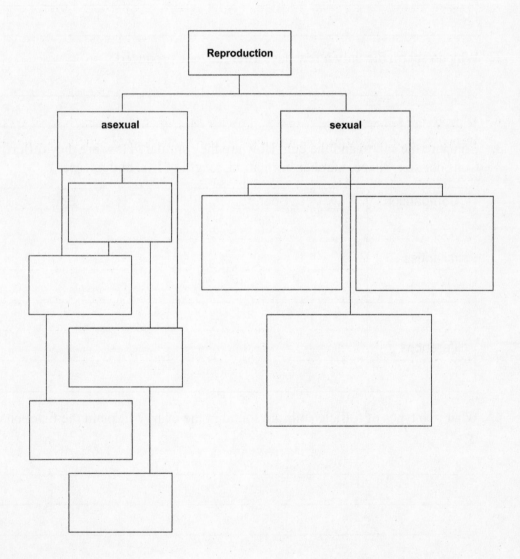

How I Am Being Assessed	_____
	_____

Understanding Concepts

1. Describe the development of sperm.

    _____

    _____

    _____

2. Why do sperm die only a few days after they are produced?

    _____

    _____

3. Compare the sperm and the egg. How are they similar? How are they different? Consider size, shape, number, formation, length of life, and release.

Comparison	Sperm	Egg
similarities		
differences		

4. What two types of follicle cells are found in the ovary? Explain the function of each type.

    _____

    _____

    _____

    _____

5. Describe ovulation.

_____

_____

_____

Making Connections

6. If the ovaries of a woman are removed, can she still give birth to a baby? Support your answer.

_____

_____

_____

_____

7. Ectopic pregnancies occur when the embryo becomes implanted in the oviduct rather than the uterus. Why is this a dangerous situation?

_____

_____

_____

_____

Work the Web

Hormones control both the male and the female reproductive systems. What are the names of these hormones, and how do they affect the development of sperm and eggs?

_____

_____

_____

_____

_____

_____

_____

How I Am Being Assessed _____

_____

Inside an Egg

An egg is a self-contained environment that frees the parent from the responsibility of carrying its developing offspring. Inside the egg are structures and membranes similar to those surrounding the human embryo. In this activity, you will examine how the egg supports the development of the embryo.

Objective

To identify the parts of an egg and examine how the egg is adapted to support an embryo.

Materials

- petri dish or saucer
- forceps or tweezers
- hand lens or magnifying glass
- unfertilized chicken egg (the bigger the better)

Procedure and Observations

1. Crack the egg open carefully, and pour it into the petri dish.

2. **Figure 1** on the next page identifies the main structures of the egg. Use the hand lens and forceps to help you find each structure. Put a check mark beside each label as you find that structure.

 Raw egg may contain bacteria. Work carefully to prevent contamination.

3. Clean up, and wash your hands well.

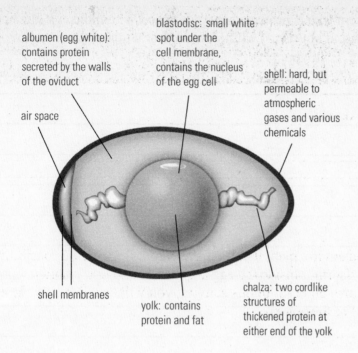

albumen (egg white): contains protein secreted by the walls of the oviduct

air space

blastodisc: small white spot under the cell membrane, contains the nucleus of the egg cell

shell: hard, but permeable to atmospheric gases and various chemicals

shell membranes

yolk: contains protein and fat

chalza: two cordlike structures of thickened protein at either end of the yolk

Figure 1
The amniotic egg is a protective, self-contained environment.

Analysis and Conclusion

(a) Often the appearance of a structure provides clues to its function. Complete the summary table below by recording the appearance of each structure in the egg and then predicting its function.

Structure	Appearance	Predicted function
shell		
shell membranes		
air space		
yolk		
albumen		
chalaza		
blastodisc		

(b) Just as the chicken embryo is protected and nourished within the egg, the human embryo is protected and nourished within the mother's uterus. Explain how, using terms from section 2.17 in your text.

_____

_____

_____

_____

_____

_____

_____

_____

_____

Can You Answer This Bonus Question?

By observing the development of a frog embryo, you can begin to appreciate how a human embryo develops. Using the Internet, draw a series of diagrams showing how the frog embryo develops in the first six days, from fertilized egg to a tadpole.

2.17 Human Conception and Implantation

Questions

Understanding Concepts

1. Describe the journey of the egg from the ovary to the uterus. Use the time line to show what happens when.

0 _____

2. Where does the placenta come from?

_____

_____

_____

3. Use the table below to compare the functions of the membranes and structures protecting the embryo: uterus, endometrium, placenta, yolk sac, amnion, amniotic fluid, umbilical cord.

Membrane or structure	Function
uterus	
endometrium	
placenta	
yolk sac	
amnion	
amniotic fluid	
umbilical cord	

Making Connections

4. The placenta begins releasing hormones after three months of pregnancy. The hormone progesterone does the following:
   - keeps the endometrium healthy
   - prevents ovulation
   - stops the uterus from contracting

(a) Predict what would happen during pregnancy if the placenta became damaged and could not maintain progesterone levels. Give reasons for your prediction.

_____

_____

_____

_____

_____

(b) Why don't women conceive again later in their pregnancy?

_____

_____

How I Am Being Assessed _____

_____

Understanding Concepts

1. Summarize the procedures used in each of the five reproductive technologies.

Name of technology	Summary
fertility drugs	
intrauterine insemination	
in vitro fertilization	
egg freezing and egg donations	
embryo transfer	

2. Explain why the old term "test-tube baby" is not accurate.

_____

_____

_____

3. Study **Figure 3** on page 107 of your text. Rearrange the following random list of statements to form the correct order of steps in vitro fertilization. Write the correct order below.

- Eggs are placed in a petri dish.
- Eggs are extracted from the ovary.
- Eggs are fertilized by sperm.
- Hormone fertility drugs are given to the woman.
- The embryo is transferred to the uterus.
- The embryo is incubated.

_____

_____

_____

_____

_____

_____

Making Connections

4. Reproductive technologies create controversy because of the ethical questions involved. Use a dictionary to define "ethical." Draw a concept map of this section, listing all the ethical questions that could be raised by each reproductive technology. Prepare a summary paragraph outlining your viewpoint on using reproductive technologies.

Definition of "ethical":

_____

_____

Summary paragraph outlining your viewpoint on using reproductive technologies:

_____

_____

_____

_____

_____

Concept map of section topics, listing ethical questions that could be raised:

☞ Work the Web

Infertility affects both males and females. Find possible causes and risk factors of infertility.

_____

_____

_____

_____

_____

_____

_____

_____

_____

_____

_____

How I Am Being Assessed _____

_____

What Happens When?

Stages of development during the nine months of pregnancy are listed below. Classify each as 1 (first), 2 (second), or 3 (third) trimester.

Development	Trimester (1, 2, 3)
The fetus puts on most of its weight during this trimester.	
Sex organs form, but gender is not yet obvious.	
Cartilage begins to be replaced by bone.	
Hair grows on the head and body.	
Body hair begins to disappear.	
A basic heart has formed and begins to beat.	
The fetus can swallow, hear, and cry.	
The fetus alternates between sleep and wake cycles.	
The fetus drinks the amniotic fluid and urinates back into it.	
Most miscarriages occur during this trimester.	
The embryo has a tail.	
Most of the skeleton has been replaced by bone.	
The mother will feel fetal movement, or "quickening."	
Eyelids, fingernails, and toenails form.	
The brain appears very large in proportion to the rest of the embryo.	
There is little room for the fetus to move in the womb.	

External sex organs become clearly male or female.	
The baby's lungs can function if it is born at this stage.	
Eyelashes form and the tongue has developed taste buds.	
The fetus is very active, kicking and stretching.	
The nervous system responds to stimuli.	
A sucking reflex appears in the mouth area.	
The fetus can blink, grasp with its fingers, and suck its thumb.	
Bones in the body begin to harden, although bones in the head stay soft.	
The embryo develops enough to be called a fetus during this trimester.	
Facial features, limbs, hands, feet, fingers, and toes become visible.	
The risk of birth defects is greatest during this trimester.	
The fetus "breathes" in the amniotic fluid.	
By the end of this trimester, the fetus resembles a miniature infant.	
The ribs and backbone are very soft.	
The fetus is shorter than your pen at the end of this trimester.	
The fetus's skin is almost see-through.	
Only about half of the fetuses born at the end of this trimester would survive.	
Limb buds first appear, then grow into arms and legs.	

Count how many times you have trimester 1 (_____), trimester 2 (_____), and trimester 3 (_____) in the table above.

In which trimester do most developmental changes occur?

_____

In which trimester do most miscarriages occur?

_____

Many women are not aware of their pregnancy until the third month. From what you
know about all the development that occurs during this time, what advice would you give
to any female of childbearing age?

_____

_____

_____

_____

_____

_____

_____

_____

_____

_____

_____

How I Am Being Assessed _____

_____

Understanding Concepts

1. Prepare a time line of the events from conception to birth. Organize this line vertically down this page. Summarize all the information from sections 2.17 and 2.19 in your text.

2. Choose one of the pieces of prenatal advice from page 110 of your text. Illustrate this advice below, using as many drawings and as few words as possible.

3. What are the differences among a zygote, an embryo, a fetus, and a baby?

_____

_____

_____

_____

_____

_____

_____

Making Connections

4. The circulatory system is the first system to function in the embryo. Use a dictionary to define "circulatory system," and then explain why you think this is the case.

_____

_____

_____

_____

5. Review the female reproductive system in section 2.16 of your text. Why does the risk of genetic disorders increase with the age of the mother?

_____

_____

_____

_____

Exploring

6. Physical signs of pregnancy are described in this section of your text. Summarize what happens in the mother during each trimester, and use an encyclopedia or medical reference for additional details. There are also chemical signs of pregnancy. Research pregnancy tests and how they work.

Physical signs of pregnancy, by trimester:

_____

_____

_____

_____

_____

_____

_____

_____

_____

Chemical signs of pregnancy (pregnancy tests):

_____

_____

_____

_____

_____

🖱 Work the Web

Choose a genetic disorder. Describe the causes, likelihood, risk factors, prevention, and symptoms of the disorder.

_____

_____

_____

_____

_____

_____

_____

_____

_____

_____

_____

2.20 Explore an Issue
Fetal Alcohol Syndrome

Take a Stand

FAS: A Preventable Problem?

Statement

Pregnant women should be required to have blood tests on a regular basis to monitor drinking problems.

What Do You Think?

- In a group, carefully read the statement and the points presented for and against it. Discuss and then write down any additional points for and against you can think of from the information given on pages 112–113 of your text.

Additional points for	Additional points against

- Search for additional information using the library, CD-ROMs, or the Internet.
- From your research, prepare a summary of additional information on the topic, and use this to form your opinion on the statement.

_____

_____

_____

_____

_____

_____

_____

_____

_____

_____

_____

_____

_____

_____

- Share the research information with your group members, and then decide whether your group agrees or disagrees with the statement.
- Write a summary of your group's final position.
- Prepare to defend your group's position in a class discussion.

_____

_____

_____

_____

_____

_____

2.20 Explore an Issue
Fetal Alcohol Syndrome

How I Am Being Assessed _____

_____

Understanding Concepts

1. What is the incidence of FAS/FAE in Canada?

    _____

    _____

2. Use this table to list the possible physical and mental characteristics of children with FAS.

Physical characteristics	Mental characteristics

Reflecting

3. How do you think the FAS problem could be solved?

    _____

    _____

    _____

    _____

    _____

Unit 2 Summary

What Have You Learned?

How I Am Being Assessed _____

_____

Revisit your answers to the What Do You Already Know? questions on page 102 in Getting Started.

Have any of your answers changed?

_____

_____

_____

_____

_____

_____

What new questions do you have?

_____

_____

_____

_____

_____

_____

How I Am Being Assessed _____

_____

Use the concept map to review the major concepts in Unit 2. This map can help you begin to organize the information that you have studied. You may add more links to your map. Also, you may add more information in each box.

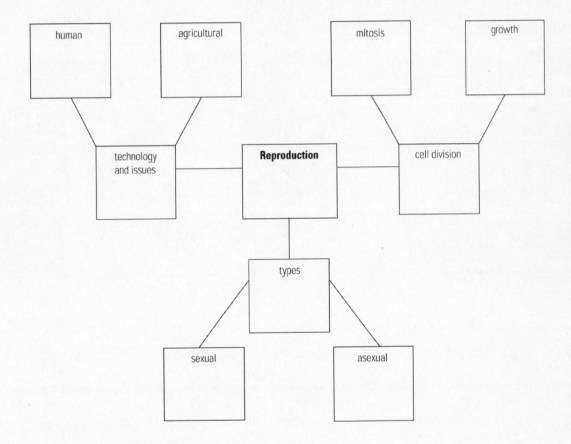

A concept map can be used to review a large topic on a general level, or it can be used to examine a very specific topic in detail. Select one concept from this unit that you need to study more, and make a detailed concept map for it in the space below.

Unit 2 Reproduction: Processes and Applications

 *Challenge*

Once you have chosen your Challenge, use the space that follows to answer the Challenge questions from your text. You may also want to use these pages to record any ideas or to draw tables, graphs, or sketches that relate to your Challenge.

Challenge	Section and page in textbook
1 Reproductive Technology	Section 2.9, page 89 Section 2.10, page 91 Section 2.12, page 95 Section 2.13, page 98 Section 2.15, page 101 Section 2.18, page 107 Section 2.19, page 111 Section 2.20, page 113
2 Plant Experiment	Section 2.1, page 71 Section 2.3, page 75 Section 2.8, page 87 Section 2.9, page 89 Section 2.12, page 95 Section 2.13, page 98 Section 2.14, page 99 Section 2.16, page 103 Section 2.17, page 105 Section 2.19, page 111 Section 2.20, page 113
3 Analyzing Cancer Risk	Section 2.2, page 73 Section 2.4, page 77 Section 2.5, page 79 Section 2.6, page 81 Section 2.7, page 83 Section 2.11, page 93 Section 2.12, page 95 Section 2.16, page 103 Section 2.20, page 113

Challenge Journal

_____

_____

_____

_____

_____

_____

_____

_____

_____

_____

_____

_____

_____

_____

_____

_____

_____

_____

_____

_____

_____

_____

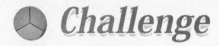 *Challenge*

Learning about Electricity

As you learn about how electricity works, you will analyze your electricity use and its impacts in everyday life. You will also be able to show your learning by completing one of the following Challenges.

1 Design and Test an Electric Circuit

Electric circuits can be used for a variety of purposes. Design and test an electric circuit that performs a job of your choice. Present the completed electric circuit to the class and explain its purpose.

2 Electrical Safety Pamphlet

Electricity can be dangerous if not used properly in the home and workplace. Create an electrical safety pamphlet outlining specific steps to follow to ensure electrical safety. Use your own home and a chosen workplace to develop this pamphlet. Include an electrical safety checklist for readers to complete.

3 Electric Game Show

Electricity is an important form of energy that we rely on. Produce a quiz board that requires information about static and current electricity, designing and building electric circuits, electricity's impact on society and the environment, and using electricity safely in our everyday lives.

Select a Challenge. Use the space on pages 296 to 298 to answer the Challenge questions from your text and to record your ideas for your challenge.

Unit 3 Getting Started

What Do You Already Know?

1. At what time of year is static electricity most active? Why do you think this is the case?

   _____

   _____

   _____

2. Describe how the following products work, in relation to static electricity. You may use pictures in your answers.

   (a) fabric softener dryer sheets

   _____

   _____

   _____

   (b) plastic cling wrap

   _____

   _____

   _____

3. What is an electric circuit?

   _____

   _____

   _____

4. What safety precautions should you follow with current electricity? List as many as you can.

_____

_____

_____

_____

_____

_____

_____

5. Name two methods of generating electrical energy.

(i) _____

_____

_____

(ii) _____

_____

_____

Think back to what you learned in earlier grades.

Complete as much as you can of the concept map below. At the end of the unit, come back to this page and either

(a) add to the concept map

(b) correct any of the information that may not be accurate

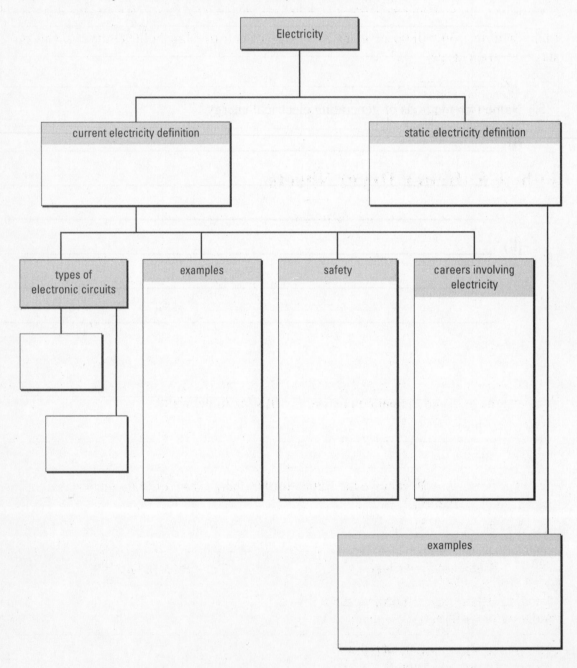

How I Am Being Assessed _____

_____

In this activity you will observe and record the effects of fabric softener dryer sheets on static electric charge.

 Do not blow the balloon too big or it will burst.

Fabric Softener Dryer Sheets

(a) Record the instructions on the package in the space below:

_____

_____

_____

_____

_____

(b) Rub a balloon on the top of your head or on your clothing to charge it. How long do you have to rub the balloon before it will stick to the wall?

_____

_____

(c) Try three ways to remove the static electric charge from the balloon. Record the results in **Table 1.**

Table 1

Fabric softener test	Observations
charged balloon placed on the fabric softener dryer sheet	
charged balloon rubbed with the fabric softener dryer sheet	
charged balloon touched with hands rubbed with fabric softener dryer sheet	

(d) Which test(s) resulted in the charged balloon not sticking to the wall?

_____

_____

_____

_____

_____

(e) How do you think a fabric softener dryer sheet works to remove static electricity from your clothes?

_____

_____

_____

_____

_____

_____

_____

3.1 Investigation
Investigating Electric Charges
Report

In this investigation, you will electrically charge a variety of substances and identify some properties of electric charges.

Question

How are uncharged and charged substances affected when they are near one another?

Prediction

(a) Predict what will happen when you bring two charged objects near one another.

_____

_____

_____

Observations

Record your observations in **Table 1.**

Table 1

Electric charge test	Effect on scraps of paper	Effect on stream of water	Effect on pith ball
ebonite rod rubbed with fur			
Lucite rod rubbed with silk or polyester			

Analysis and Conclusion

(b) Was your prediction correct? Explain why, or why not, based on your observations.

_____

_____

_____

(c) Compare the results of the investigation for the ebonite and Lucite rods on the scraps of paper, water stream, and pith ball.

_____

_____

_____

(d) What happens when charged objects are placed near uncharged objects?

_____

_____

_____

(e) What happens to the force between charged and uncharged objects as the distance between them decreases? Support your answer with observations from the investigation.

_____

_____

_____

(f) List the properties of electric charges you have identified in this investigation.

_____

_____

_____

_____

How I Am Being Assessed _____

_____

Making Connections

1. From your observations, what can you say about what happens when charged objects are brought close to uncharged objects?

   _____

   _____

   _____

   _____

   _____

2. Describe a test that you could perform to determine whether an object is charged or uncharged.

   _____

   _____

   _____

   _____

   _____

3. How does an anti-static dryer sheet work? Explain it in terms of electric charges.

   _____

   _____

   _____

   _____

4. Why do people get shocks after they drag their feet on a rug? Explain it in terms of electric charges.

_____

_____

_____

_____

Reflecting

5. Record in the chart below three different situations in which you have experienced the effects of static electricity. Beside each, write down what pairs of materials you think might be responsible for producing static electricity.

Static electricity example	Materials responsible

Outline the online investigation carried out in this Work the Web. What conclusions can you draw from it?

Investigation	Conclusions

3.2 Electricity and Matter

Questions

How I Am Being Assessed _____

_____

Understanding Concepts

1. Are all objects electrically charged? Explain.

   _____

   _____

   _____

   _____

   _____

2. What is static electricity? Describe a situation involving static electricity to explain your answer.

   _____

   _____

   _____

   _____

   _____

3. Explain in detail how you could demonstrate the law of electric charges.

   _____

   _____

   _____

   _____

   _____

4. What is the difference between static electricity and current electricity? Include examples of each in your answer.

_____

_____

_____

_____

_____

Making Connections

5. You are normally uncharged, or neutral. You drag your feet on a rug and shock an unsuspecting friend by touching his or her ear.

   (a) Why does your friend feel a shock?

   _____

   _____

   _____

   (b) What can you do to stop the buildup of static electric charge as you drag your feet on the rug?

   _____

   _____

   _____

Reflecting

6. What happens when ebonite is rubbed with fur and Lucite is rubbed with silk or polyester? Explain your answer in terms of the law of electric charges.

_____

_____

_____

_____

_____

How I Am Being Assessed _____

_____

In this investigation, you will use a pith ball apparatus to determine the kind of charge transferred from one object to another.

Question

How can we determine the kind of charge transferred to a neutral object when a charged object touches it?

 If you are allergic to fur, you should not perform this investigation.

Prediction

(a) Use the law of electric charges to predict what kind of charge is transferred from each object to a pith ball apparatus.

_____

_____

_____

_____

Observations

(b)-(d) Record your observations in **Table 1** below.

Table 1

Action	Observations
charged ebonite rod brought close to pith ball but does not touch	
charged ebonite rod touches the pith ball and is then brought close	
charged Lucite rod brought close to the pith ball but does not touch	
charged Lucite rod touches the pith ball and is then brought close	

Analysis and Conclusion

(e) Write a statement about the transfer of electric charge when the pith ball is touched by a

   (i) negatively charged object

   (ii) positively charged object

Explain your answers.

(i) _____

_____

_____

_____

(ii) _____

_____

_____

_____

(f) Why was the pith ball repelled by the charged ebonite rod after being touched? Your explanation should include a drawing.

_____

_____

_____

_____

_____

Drawing:

(g) Why was the pith ball repelled by the charged Lucite rod after being touched? Your explanation should include a drawing.

_____

_____

_____

_____

_____

Drawing:

(h) Write a statement to compare the movement of electric charges in the ebonite rod and the Lucite rod.

_____

_____

_____

_____

_____

_____

How I Am Being Assessed _____

_____

Understanding Concepts

1. If your hand were negatively charged and you touched a neutral doorknob, in which direction would negative charges move? Explain your answer.

_____

_____

_____

_____

Exploring

2. Use two pith ball apparatuses and predict, observe, and explain what happens when they are brought close together if

   (a) they are charged alike

   (b) they have opposite charges

   (c) one is charged and the other is not

Use simple diagrams to explain what you observe.

Prediction

Pith balls	Prediction
charged alike	
opposite charges	
one is charged and the other is not	

Observations and Explanation

Pith balls	Prediction
charged alike	
opposite charges	
one is charged and the other is not	

_____

_____

_____

Reflecting

3. How could charging by contact be used to paint a car?

_____

_____

_____

_____

_____

Work the Web

List safety precautions that you should take if caught outside in a lightning storm.

_____

_____

_____

_____

_____

_____

_____

_____

3.4 What Is Electric Current?

Try This Activity

How I Am Being Assessed _____

_____

Comparing Water Flow to the Flow of Electric Current

Comparing water flow in a plumbing system to the flow of electric current in an electric circuit is best explained through a demonstration. In this activity, you will need a partner, a retort stand, two funnels of different sizes, cotton, water, two plastic containers, and a sketchpad. You must observe, record, and communicate to your partner how a plumbing system is like electric current flowing in an electric circuit.

(a) Explain how you would use the water flow to demonstrate a low-voltage electric current.

_____

_____

_____

_____

_____

How would you demonstrate a high-voltage electric current?

_____

_____

_____

_____

(b) How would you change the funnel to represent an electrical wire that has a high-current capacity—the ability to carry more electric current?

_____

_____

_____

_____

How would you represent a low-current capacity?

_____

_____

_____

_____

(c) How could you use the funnel to represent an electrical line that has decreased resistance to the flow of electric current?

_____

_____

_____

_____

How would you represent a line that has increased resistance to the flow of current?

_____

_____

_____

_____

3.4 What Is Electric Current? Questions

How I Am Being Assessed _____

_____

Understanding Concepts

1. What are the two main parts of an electric current?

    _____

    _____

    _____

    _____

    _____

2. Explain, in your own words, how electric current, voltage, and resistance are like water flowing in a plumbed water system.

    _____

    _____

    _____

    _____

    _____

    _____

    _____

    _____

    _____

    _____

3. How much electric current is needed to kill a human being? Explain.

    _____

    _____

    _____

    _____

    _____

4. List three devices from **Table 2** on page 135 of your textbook that you use in your home. Order the devices from largest to smallest, in terms of their electric current ratings.

_____

_____

_____

_____

Exploring

5. The use of electricity in a house can be made "safer" in many ways. Research the topic of home electrical safety, using the library or Internet resources, and prepare an oral report for the class.

_____

_____

_____

_____

_____

_____

_____

_____

_____

Work the Web

Explain how you could help a victim of electric shock.

_____

_____

_____

_____

_____

_____

3.5 Activity
The Electric Circuit

How I Am Being Assessed _____

_____

In this activity, you will construct and test various simple electric circuits.

Question

How are the parts connected to create a working electric circuit?

Observations

Use **Table 1** to record your observations.

Table 1

Load used	Diagram of circuit
light bulb	
electric motor	
LED (light emitting diode)	

(a) What is the voltage rating of the battery?

_____

_____

_____

(b)-(d)   Sketch the steps carried out to produce a working electric circuit with a light bulb, an electric motor, and a LED in **Table 1**.

(e) What is the function of the (i) dry cell, (ii) switch, (iii) light bulb, (iv) electric motor, (v) LED, and (vi) wires? Record your answers in **Table 2**.

Table 2

Electric parts	Function
(i) dry cell	
(ii) switch	
(iii) light bulb	
(iv) electric motor	
(v) LED	
(vi) wires	

(f) Which of the four parts of the electric circuit can be removed while allowing the circuit to continue working? Why is it usually included in a circuit?

_____

_____

_____

(g) List three different ways of turning the electrical devices (light bulb, electric motor, LED) on or off.

_____

_____

_____

(h) Would the circuit operate differently if the connections on the switch were reversed? if the switch were connected on the other side of the electrical device? If you are not sure, try making the changes. Explain your answers. You can include diagrams in your answer.

- the connections on the switch were reversed?

_____

_____

_____

Diagram:

- the switch were connected on the other side of the electrical device?

_____

_____

_____

Diagram:

3.5 Activity: The Electric Circuit **223**

(i) What effect would reversing the connecting wires have on the light bulb? the electric motor? the LED? Explain your answer. Test your answers, if possible.

- the light bulb

  _____

  _____

  _____

- the electric motor

  _____

  _____

  _____

- the LED

  _____

  _____

  _____

6. An important part of any electric circuit is the energy source. Different energy sources are used for different purposes. Identify a common use for each type of batteries in **Figure 4** on page 140 of your textbook. Use **Table 3** to record your answers.

Table 3

Battery Type	Use
AA	
AAA	
D	
9V	
lantern battery	
small circular battery	

7. **Figure 5** on page 140 of your textbook is an example of how an electric circuit can be used on a bicycle. The small, specially shaped batteries on these bicycles can be recharged each night.

(j) What are the four main parts of the electric circuit in this device?

_____

_____

_____

_____

3.5 Activity
The Electric Circuit

How I Am Being Assessed _____

_____

Understanding Concepts

1. How do you know whether you have a complete electric circuit?

   _____

   _____

   _____

   _____

2. Explain, in your own words, the steps to follow to build electric circuits.

   _____

   _____

   _____

3. What was the voltage rating of the battery used in this activity? Do all batteries have the same voltage? Explain.

   _____

   _____

   _____

4. Draw a working electric circuit with the four main parts labelled: (i) source of electrical energy, (ii) electrical load (device), (iii) electric circuit control device (switch), and (iv) connectors.

Making Connections

5. Identify and describe three kinds of switches:

    (a) in your home

    _____

    _____

    (b) on electrical devices you use every day

    _____

    _____

    (c) in a car

    _____

    _____

    Suggest reasons why different switches are used in different situations.

    _____

    _____

    _____

    _____

    _____

6. Think about toys that need batteries to work properly.

    (a) What problems could you have with the electric parts of these toys?

    _____

    _____

    _____

    (b) How do you know when the batteries need to be replaced? Be specific.

    _____

    _____

    _____

(c) Have batteries become more reliable? Explain.

_____

_____

_____

Exploring

7. Predict what could happen if more than one electrical device were hooked up in a row in your electric circuit. Try it, and comment on your prediction.

_____

_____

_____

_____

_____

_____

Work the Web

Outline the online investigations carried out in this Work the Web. What conclusions can you draw from it?

Investigation	Conclusions

3.6 Series and Parallel Circuits   *Extension Activity*

How I Am Being Assessed _____

_____

An electric circuit can be represented in several ways. Circuit diagrams represent one way, and drawing the actual parts of a circuit is another way. A third way is to build a model. In this activity, you will use available materials to build models for two circuits.

Materials

- string
- cardboard
- markers
- glue
- other materials as required

Procedure

1. Cut out two pieces of cardboard that are 20 cm by 20 cm.

2. Develop a legend that will show what materials will represent the various parts of the electric circuits being built. Complete the list below.

Part of electric circuit	Material used in model
wire	string
dry cell	
motor	
light	
switch	

3. Build a model of a series circuit that has the following parts:

   - 2 lights
   - 2 dry cells
   - 1 switch
   - 3 motors

4. Build a parallel circuit that contains the following components:

   - 3 lights
   - 1 motor
   - a switch to control each load in the circuit
   - 4 dry cells

5. Make sure that the models follow the legend you created.

6. Label the parts in each model.

7. Present the models to the class.

Analysis and Conclusion

1. What advantages do models of electric circuits have over circuit diagrams?

   _____

   _____

   _____

   _____

2. What advantages do circuit diagrams have over models of electric circuits?

   _____

   _____

   _____

   _____

3. Are more materials used in creating a parallel or a series circuit? Explain your answer.

   _____

   _____

   _____

   _____

4. Where else are models used in science? List one example and explain its use.

   _____

   _____

   _____

   _____

How I Am Being Assessed _____

_____

Understanding Concepts

1. Explain, in your own words, the differences between a series and a parallel circuit.

   _____

   _____

   _____

   _____

   _____

2. What is a circuit diagram?

   _____

   _____

   _____

3. Draw circuit diagrams for the following circuits:

   (a) two cells, one open switch, and a light wired in series

   (b) one cell, two lights, and a clock wired in parallel

(c) a series circuit of your own design

(d) a parallel circuit of your own design

Making Connections

4. Why are homes wired in parallel? Give two reasons.

_____

_____

_____

_____

_____

5. Why are battery-operated toys wired in series?

_____

_____

_____

_____

_____

Exploring

6. Draw a circuit diagram for one room of your home. Remember that your home is wired in parallel.

Reflecting

7. Why are circuit diagrams used rather than drawings of the actual parts of a circuit?

_____

_____

_____

_____

How I Am Being Assessed _____

_____

Complete the graphic organizer below to summarize the key concepts presented to this point. Add more boxes if needed and include at least two examples of each type of electricity.

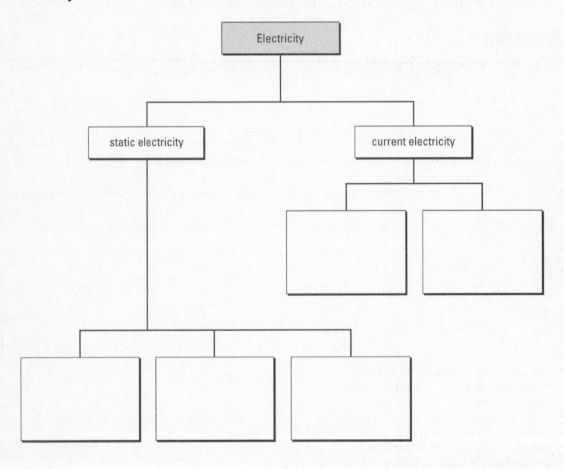

3.7 Investigation
Building Parallel and Series Circuits

Report

In this investigation, you will build and compare series and parallel circuits.

Question

How can you determine the characteristics of parallel and series circuits?

Prediction

(a) Write one or more predictions about what you think will happen in series and parallel circuits.

_____

_____

Observations

(b)-(f) Use **Table 1** to record your observations.

Table 1

Action	Observations
comparison of bulb brightness in series/parallel circuits (two bulbs, one dry cell)	
comparison of bulb brightness in series/parallel circuits (two bulbs, two dry cells)	
removal of one bulb in the series circuit	
removal of one bulb in the parallel circuit	

Analysis and Conclusion

(g) Compare the brightness of the two bulbs in the series and parallel circuits (one dry cell). In which circuit were the lights brighter?

_____

_____

(h) A light bulb was removed from the series circuit in step 4. Why did all the lights go out?

_____

_____

(i) A light bulb was removed from the parallel circuit in step 4. Why did the other lights stay on?

_____

_____

(j) In step 5, light bulbs were added to the series circuit. Explain what happened to the brightness of the light bulbs as light bulbs were added.

_____

_____

(k) In step 6, light bulbs were added to the parallel circuit. Explain what happened to the brightness of the light bulbs as light bulbs were added.

_____

_____

(l) In a series circuit, is it possible to switch a single device on or off? Why?

_____

_____

(m) In a parallel circuit, is it possible to switch a single device on or off? Why?

_____

_____

How I Am Being Assessed _____

_____

Understanding Concepts

1. Why would a string of lights, such as the ones used to decorate trees, be wired in series?

   _____

   _____

   _____

2. What is an advantage of wiring electric circuits in parallel? What is a disadvantage?

   _____

   _____

   _____

3. What is an advantage of wiring electric circuits in series? What is a disadvantage?

   _____

   _____

   _____

4. Draw a circuit diagram of a cell connected in parallel with two lights and a motor, with each electrical device controlled by a switch.

Making Connections

5. Light bulbs represent electrical resistance in a circuit.

   (a) What happens when electrical resistance is added in a series circuit?

   _____

   _____

   (b) What happens when electrical resistance is added in a parallel circuit?

   _____

   _____

6. **(a)** Suppose 15 light bulbs were connected in series, and one bulb burned out. How could you find the defective bulb?

   _____

   _____

   _____

   (b) How could you identify one defective bulb if the 15 bulbs are connected in parallel? Explain.

   _____

   _____

   _____

Work the Web

How did you do? Summarize your knowledge about parallel and series circuits after completing the online quiz.

_____

_____

_____

_____

_____

_____

_____

3.8 Measuring Voltage Drop and Current

How I Am Being Assessed _____

_____

Understanding Concepts

1. How are a voltmeter and an ammeter arranged differently in a circuit?

   _____

   _____

   _____

   _____

   _____

2. Draw a circuit diagram of a dry cell, an open switch, a light bulb, and a voltmeter connected across a light bulb.

Copyright © 2003 Nelson   *3.8 Measuring Voltage Drop and Current* **239**

3. Draw a circuit diagram of the same electrical circuit in question 2, but insert an ammeter after the light bulb.

Making Connections

4. When would an electrician use a voltmeter? When would an electrician use an ammeter?

_____

_____

_____

_____

5. Homes in Canada are supplied with electricity at 120 V. What might a reading lower than 120 V mean?

_____

_____

_____

Exploring

6. Electrical devices are labelled with their current ratings. Find the current ratings of four different devices in your home. Make sure that the devices are unplugged.

Electrical device	Current (A)

Which device requires the most current?

_____

_____

_____

3.9 Investigation
Report

Comparing Current and Voltage Drop in an Electric Circuit

How I Am Being Assessed _____

_____

In this investigation, you will design, build, and measure electric current and voltage drop for series and parallel circuits.

Question

How can you accurately measure voltage drop and electric current in series and parallel circuits?

Prediction

(a) Write a prediction for this investigation.

_____

_____

_____

Observations

(b)-(f) Use **Table 1** to record your observations for Part 1: Electrical Loads in a Parallel Circuit.

(g)-(l) Use **Table 2** to record your observations for Part 2: Electrical Loads in a Series Circuit.

Table 1: **Electrical Loads in a Parallel Circuit**

Number of bulbs	Voltage (V) across battery	Voltage (V) across bulb	Current (A)
1			
2			
3			

Observations when bulbs were removed and replaced:

Light bulbs	Observations
removal of bulb #1 replacement of bulb #1	
removal of bulb #2 replacement of bulb #2	
removal of bulb #3 replacement of bulb #3	

Table 2: Electrical Loads in a Series Circuit

Number of bulbs	Voltage (V) across battery	Voltage (V) across bulb	Current (A)
1			
2			
3			

Observations when bulbs were removed and replaced:

Removal and replacement of light bulbs	Observations
1	
2	
3	

Analysis and Conclusion

(m) Analyze your observations by answering the following questions for Parts 1 and 2:

(i) How does the voltage drop across the dry cell compare with the voltage drop across each of the three bulbs?

Part 1: Parallel Circuit

_____

_____

_____

_____

_____

Part 2: Series Circuit

_____

_____

_____

_____

_____

(ii) What happens to the brightness of the light from the bulbs as a new bulb is added?

Part 1: Parallel Circuit

_____

_____

_____

_____

_____

Part 2: Series Circuit

_____

_____

_____

_____

_____

(iii) What happens when you unscrew one of the bulbs?

Part 1: Parallel Circuit

_____

_____

_____

_____

_____

Part 2: Series Circuit

_____

_____

_____

_____

(iv) How many paths for current flow does each circuit have?

Part 1: Parallel Circuit

_____

_____

_____

_____

_____

Part 2: Series Circuit

_____

_____

_____

_____

_____

3.9 Investigation
Comparing Current and Voltage Drop in an Electric Circuit

Questions

How I Am Being Assessed _____

_____

Understanding Concepts

1. Is electric current shared in a series circuit? Explain your answer by referring to your observations.

   _____

   _____

   _____

2. Which part of the sign in **Figure 3** on page 149 of your textbook is wired in series? Which part is wired in parallel?

   _____

   _____

   _____

   _____

Making Connections

3. Explain, in your own words, how to measure current in a circuit.

   _____

   _____

   _____

4. Explain, in your own words, how to measure the voltage drop across an electrical load in a circuit.

   _____

   _____

   _____

   _____

3.10 Case Study
Electrical Resistance

Report

How I Am Being Assessed _____

_____

(a) Resistance changes electrical energy into one of four forms of energy. What are they?

_____

_____

_____

_____

(b) Define voltage drop. What unit is used to measure voltage drop?

_____

_____

_____

_____

(c) Define current. What unit is used to measure current?

_____

_____

_____

_____

(d) How do you think resistance affects electrical devices?

_____

_____

_____

_____

(e) Look at **Table 1**. Notice that the voltage drop does not change. What pattern do you notice for current and resistance?

_____

_____

_____

_____

Table 1 **Resistance of Some Electrical Loads**

Ohm's Law	V	=	I	×	R

Load	Voltage drop (V)	Current (A)	Resistance (□)
light bulb (60 W)	120	0.50	240
coffee grinder	120	1.20	100
food dehydrator	120	4.60	26
toaster oven	120	14.0	8.6

Look at the circuit shown in **Figure 7** on page 152 of your textbook. The resistor in the diagram has a resistance of 10 Ω. The ammeter reads 2 A. The voltage drop is constant.

(f) Will the ammeter reading go up or down if a 5 Ω resistor replaces the 10 Ω resistor?

_____

_____

_____

_____

(g) Complete the sentence. If the voltage drop is constant and the resistance increases, the current _____. If the voltage drop is constant and the resistance decreases, the current _____.

Are You Resistant?

Most multimeters can measure electrical resistance, as well as voltage and current. Set the meter to its resistance scale, and hold one tip of each lead in each hand.

Use **Table 1** to record your resistance measurements.

Table 1

Hands	Resistance (Ω)
dry	
wet	

What safety issues does this activity identify?

_____

_____

_____

_____

How I Am Being Assessed _____

_____

Understanding Concepts

1. Why are electric circuits important?

   _____

   _____

   _____

   _____

2. What is electrical resistance?

   _____

   _____

   _____

   _____

3. Define, in your own words, a conductor and a resistor.

   _____

   _____

   _____

   _____

4. Does the wire in the electrical cord of an electric kettle have a higher or lower resistance than the heating element inside the kettle? Explain your answer.

   _____

   _____

   _____

   _____

5. Which of the two circuits on page 153 of your textbook will have the greatest current? Explain why.

_____

_____

_____

_____

Making Connections

6. Outline four examples each of devices that transform electrical energy into:

(i) heat

_____

_____

_____

_____

(ii) light

_____

_____

_____

_____

(iii) sound

_____

_____

_____

_____

(iv) mechanical energy

_____

_____

_____

_____

Exploring

7. Using several different magazines, make a collage of photos that show the different ways that electrical resistance is used.

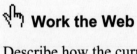 **Work the Web**

Describe how the current changes when the voltage is charged and when the resistance is charged.

_____

_____

_____

_____

_____

3.11 Investigation

The Effect of Resistance on an Electric Circuit

How I Am Being Assessed _____

_____

In this investigation, you will test the effect of different loads on the voltage drop within an electric circuit.

Question

How will voltage readings change in an electric circuit when different loads are used?

Prediction

(a) Predict what will happen to the voltage as you add light bulbs or resistors in series in a circuit.

_____

_____

Observation

(b)-(g) **Table 1** to record your observations.

Table 1

Load	Voltage drop (V) around load
1 light	
2 lights	
3 lights	
resistor 1 _____ Ω	
resistor 2 _____ Ω	
resistor 3 _____ Ω	

Predict the difference in the overall resistance in a parellel circuit as compared to a series circuit. Will it be higher or lower in a parellel circuit?

_____

_____

_____

(h)-(i) Use **Table 2** to record your observations.

Table 2

Load	Voltage drop (v)	Current (A)
2 lights in series		
2 lights in parllel		

Analysis and Conclusion

(j) What effect did the addition of light bulbs have on the brightness of each bulb?

_____

_____

_____

_____

_____

(k) Use the data obtained in **Table 1** to create a graph in which the x-axis represents the number of lights and the y-axis represents the voltage drop.

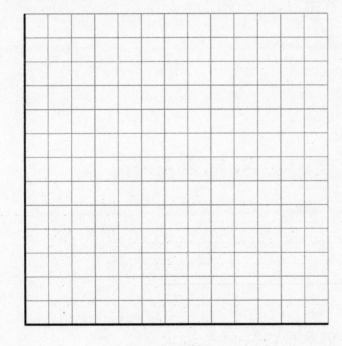

Voltage Drop (V)

Number of Lights

(l) What happened to the voltage readings when you added lights to the series circuit?

_____

_____

_____

_____

Was this what you thought would happen? Explain.

_____

_____

_____

_____

(m) Use the data in **Table 1** to create a graph in which the _x_-axis represents the size of resistor and the _y_-axis represents the voltage drop.

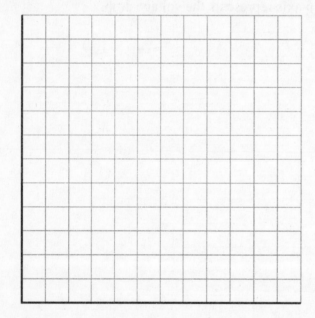

Voltage Drop (V)

Size of Resistor (Ω)

(n) Compare your results for the voltage readings of the three resistors in the series circuit. What statement could you make regarding increasing resistance and voltage values in a series circuit?

_____

_____

_____

(o) Why was the switch kept open while you built the series circuit?

_____

_____

(p) Compare the graph lines from the light bulb and the resistor data. Which has the greater voltage drop (V): resistors or light bulbs?

_____

_____

(q) Based on the voltage amd current readings in the two circuits in Part 3, do you think the overall resistance in the parellel circuit is greater than the overall resistance in the series circuit? Explain why you think so. (Hint: How did the voltages compare in the two circuits? What happened to the current?)

_____

_____

_____

3.11 Investigation: The Effect of Resistance on an Electric Circuit

3.11 Investigation

The Effect of Resistance on an Electric Circuit

Questions

How I Am Being Assessed _____

_____

Understanding Concepts

1. Explain, in your own words, the effect of resistance on voltage drop (V) ratings around a specific load in a simple electric circuit.

   _____

   _____

   _____

2. If the resistance of an electrical load were greater than the voltage available, what would happen to the circuit?

   _____

   _____

   _____

   _____

3. How was the voltmeter connected in this investigation?

   _____

   _____

   _____

   _____

   _____

Making Connections

4. Most electrical appliances have resistors (**Figure 3** on page 156 of your textbook) inside their circuits. Based on how resistors affected the voltage drop in the circuits in this investigation, explain why circuits have resistors.

_____

_____

_____

_____

5. The wires that carried the electric current in this investigation were quite thin. Resistance decreases as the thickness of the wire increases. Why are transmission wires (**Figure 4** on page 156 of your textbook) thin?

_____

_____

_____

_____

6. Based on your observations made in this investigation, what kind of circuit (series or parallel) would be most suitable to connect all the light bulbs on each of the trees in **Figure 5** on page 156 of your textbook?

_____

_____

_____

_____

7. Suppose you had to replace a burned-out bulb in a flashlight. Describe at least two ways that you could determine the correct voltage rating for the bulb.

_____

_____

_____

_____

3.11 Investigation: The Effect of Resistance on an Electric Circuit

3.12 Career Profile
Home Security Systems Installer

Questions

How I Am Being Assessed _____

_____

Making Connections

1. Home security is just one area of specialization in electricity. Use newspaper job advertisements, the Internet, or the library to learn about other careers that apply the principles of electricity.

Career	How the principles of electricity are applied in this area

2. Research the technology that is used for electrically monitored security in homes and businesses. What are the basic pieces of equipment needed to provide security surveillance?

_____

_____

_____

_____

_____

Work the Web

List questions that you have about a career as a home security systems installer.

_____

_____

_____

_____

_____

_____

_____

_____

_____

_____

_____

_____

_____

_____

How I Am Being Assessed _____

_____

Home Electrical Safety Checklist

Complete the following electrical safety checklist about your home. Based on this checklist, prepare a short report that summarizes what you can do to improve electrical safety in your home.

Electrical safety tip	What is being done in your home
Electrical outlets that are not in use should have a safety plug in the slots.	
Electrical appliances, such as hair dryers and curling irons, should be kept away from water and out of reach of children.	
Electrical extension cords should only be used temporarily. If full-time use is required, a plug should be installed instead.	
Extension cords are not placed under a rug when in use.	
The location of the distribution panel is clearly labelled and can be easily found by an electrician.	
GFCI (ground fault circuit interrupter) outlets are used in those areas of the home that are near water or are damp.	
Electrical appliances, when not in use, are left unplugged from outlets.	
Electrical heaters are never left unattended when being used.	

Report

Summarize your home electrical safety results in the space below, and answer this question: What can be done to improve electrical safety in your home?

_____

_____

_____

_____

_____

_____

_____

_____

_____

_____

_____

_____

_____

_____

_____

_____

_____

_____

How I Am Being Assessed _____

_____

Understanding Concepts

1. What are the three different wires found in most homes? What is the purpose of each?

    _____

    _____

    _____

    _____

    _____

2. Compare the advantages and disadvantages of circuit breakers and fuses.

Electrical control device	Advantages	Disadvantages
circuit breakers		
fuses		

3. List three safety features related to wall outlets, plugs, and grounding pins, and explain how they provide protection.

    _____

    _____

    _____

    _____

    _____

Making Connections

4. Complete a GFCI survey of your home. Indicate where GFCIs are installed. Record where GFCIs should be installed if they are not already there.

Location of GFCIs in home:

_____

_____

_____

_____

_____

Where GFCIs should be installed in the home (if not already there):

_____

_____

_____

_____

5. Why would having too many outlets on one circuit cause problems?

_____

_____

_____

_____

Exploring

6. List all the electrically operated safety devices in your home. Are they self-contained, or are they plugged into wall outlets? How do they function? What warning system alerts you if they stop working?

Electrically operated safety devices	Self-contained? (Y/N)	Plugged into wall outlet? (Y/N)	Function (description)	Warning system (description)

Unit 3 *What Have You Learned So Far?*

Complete the graphic organizer below to summarize the key concepts presented to this point. Add more boxes if needed.

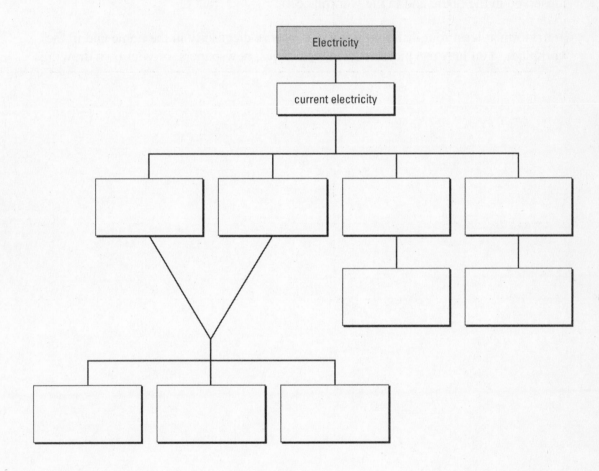

How I Am Being Assessed _____

_____

Energy Conservation Poster

In this activity, you will create a poster to answer this question: How can electricity be conserved in the home and in the workplace?

Brainstorm at least four different ways to conserve electricity in the home and in the workplace. You may use pictures from magazines, newspapers, or your own drawings.

How I Am Being Assessed _____
_____

Maximizing the Use of Electricity in the Home

1. Refer to **Table 3** (on page 163 of your textbook) and prepare common sense recommendations for using appliances in an energy-efficient manner. Use **Table 4** to record your recommendations.

Table 4

Category	Appliance example	Recommendation
heating/cooling	a. b. c. d.	
light	a. b. c. d.	
sound	a. b. c. d.	
mechanical energy	a. b. c. d.	

2. Create an advertisement that suggests ways to use electricity efficiently.

How I Am Being Assessed _____

_____

Making Connections

1. **(a)** What do you think is your family's least efficient use of electricity?

_____

_____

_____

_____

_____

(b) List three things that you could do to use electricity more efficiently in your home.

_____

_____

_____

_____

2. Do you think we will run out of electricity? Why or why not?

_____

_____

_____

_____

_____

_____

_____

_____

_____

🖐 Work the Web

Summarize in a paragraph what you learned about electricity conservation in the home and workplace.

_____

_____

_____

_____

_____

_____

3.15 Activity
The Family Energy Audit
Report

In this activity, you will collect and analyze information about the use of electrical energy in your home (or the home of a friend or a relative), identify the use of the devices as essential or nonessential, and develop a plan to maximize the efficient use of electricity.

Procedure

1. Brainstorm a list of electrical appliances used in your home. Identify the use of each device as essential or nonessential.

   (a) Use **Table 2** to record your results.

Table 2

Electrical appliance	Essential	Nonessential

2. Predict which appliances you think your family will use most, and which device will use the most energy during the monitoring period. Use **Table 1** on page 164 of your textbook as a reference point.

   (b) Record your predictions.

   _____

   _____

   _____

   _____

   _____

(c) Record the amount of time (in hours) each electrical appliance is used per day in **Table 3**.

Table 3

Electrical appliance	Time used per day (h)	Observations (family activities, weather, other events)

4. During the monitoring period, note your family's activities, the weather, and other events that might affect the amount of electricity used.

(d) Record these activities and events in **Table 3**.

5. Calculate which appliances were used the most during the monitoring period.

(e) Record your answers.

_____

_____

_____

_____

_____

6. Share your observations with a partner. Discuss your categories and how your family used the electrical devices.

(f) Did your partner have a similar viewpoint? Record any comments and any differences between your list and your partner's, giving reasons for the differences where possible.

_____

_____

_____

_____

(g) How did your predictions compare with your actual results? Comment on any differences.

_____

_____

_____

_____

(h) Review the data in the tables and suggest reasons for any unusual changes in the daily use of electrical appliances by your family.

_____

_____

_____

_____

7. Try to indentify ways to conserve energy.

_____

_____

_____

(i) Write a brief proposal to your family, making suggestions about how to reduce the electricity bill.

_____

_____

_____

_____

_____

_____

_____

_____

_____

_____

How I Am Being Assessed _____

_____

Making Connections

1. How would you convince your family that your plan is reasonable and worth following?

   _____

   _____

   _____

   _____

2. What other resources, in addition to electricity, would be conserved if your plan were put into action?

   _____

   _____

   _____

Exploring

3. Visit some environmental websites on the Internet for additional suggestions about conserving electricity.

   _____

   _____

   _____

   _____

   _____

   _____

   _____

   _____

4. Prepare a questionnaire that asks for the most important electrical appliances in a house by room. Give it to ten people. What were the most popular answers? Do your findings match your own ratings? Why do you think that is?

Room	Most important electrical appliance
kitchen	
bedroom	
living room	
laundry room	
bathroom	

_____

_____

_____

_____

_____

3.16 Efficiency and Electrical Devices

How I Am Being Assessed _____

_____

Understanding Concepts

1. Explain why energy conversions can never be 100% efficient.

   _____

   _____

   _____

   _____

   _____

2. What is the difference between input energy and useful output energy?

   _____

   _____

   _____

   _____

   _____

3. Calculate the percent efficiency of an electric motor that uses 15 000 J of energy to produce 11 500 J of useful energy.

   Energy input:

   Useful energy output:

   Percent efficiency: _____?

---

4. Calculate the percent efficiency of an incandescent light bulb that produces 2500 J of light energy from 50 000 J of electrical energy.

Energy input:

Useful energy output:

Percent efficiency: _____ ?

Making Connections

5. Why do you think it is important to be able to calculate percent efficiency?

_____

_____

_____

_____

_____

6. Provide one example each of useful output energy using the table below.

Useful output energy	Example
sound	
light	
mechanical energy	

3.17 Case Study
Automobiles and the Fuel Cell

Report

How I Am Being Assessed _____

_____

(a) Why did gas-powered automobiles replace the steam- and electric-powered cars?

_____

_____

_____

_____

_____

(b) How are the batteries connected (series or parallel) in **Figure 2** on page 168 of your textbook? Explain.

_____

_____

_____

_____

_____

(c) List the problems that must be fixed to make a practical electric vehicle.

_____

_____

_____

_____

_____

(d) What are the advantages of HEVs compared to vehicles with only gas engines?

_____

_____

_____

(e) Why are HEVs not a permanent solution to replacing vehicles with gas engines?

_____

_____

_____

_____

_____

_____

(f) What have governments done to encourage manufacturers to produce electric cars?

_____

_____

_____

_____

(g) Why are fuel cells the most likely power source for the vehicles that we will drive in the future?

_____

_____

_____

_____

(h) Why would it be helpful if fuel cells ran on the methane produced from sewage treatment plants and landfill sites?

_____

_____

_____

_____

3.17 Case Study

Questions

Automobiles and the Fuel Cell

How I Am Being Assessed _____

_____

Making Connections

1. Brainstorm a list of other practical applications for fuel cell technology.

   _____

   _____

   _____

   _____

2. What other raw materials could provide the hydrogen needed to run a fuel cell? How could this be useful for farms in isolated areas?

   _____

   _____

   _____

Exploring

3. Research on the Internet and in the library to find out more about fuel cells. Will the future energy source that powers vehicles be fuel cells? What are the advantages and disadvantages of this technology?

Advantages of fuel cells	Disadvantages of fuel cells

How I Am Being Assessed _____

_____

Risk-Benefit Analysis of Sources of Energy

As you study the various ways of generating electricity with renewable and nonrenewable energy sources on pages 170 to 172 of your textbook, add this information to the table below. Use the Internet, the library, or other resources to help you make a recommendation based on your analysis. Refer to section K of the Skills Handbook that summarizes risk-benefit analysis.

Risks				Benefits			
Possible result	Rank of that result (scale of 1-5)	Probability of that result happening	Probability value (rank x probability)	Possible result	Rank of that result (scale of 1-5)	Probability of that result happening	Probability value (rank x probability)
Total probability values (risks)				**Total probability value (benefits)**			

Which energy source would you recommend? Why?

_____

_____

_____

_____

How I Am Being Assessed _____

_____

Understanding Concepts

1. Electricity sources were compared using cost, efficiency, geography, storage, and impact on the environment.

   (a) Which energy sources were the most cost effective? the least cost effective?

   _____

   _____

   _____

   (b) Which energy sources were the most efficient? the least efficient?

   _____

   _____

   _____

   (c) Could at least one of the energy sources be used in Canada, no matter the location? Explain

   _____

   _____

   _____

   (d) Why is storage of electricity a problem?

   _____

   _____

   _____

(e) Which energy sources are the most environmentally friendly?

_____

_____

_____

2. Why is most electricity produced from nonrenewable sources in Canada?

_____

_____

_____

3. Why is the locaton of the place where the electricity is generated so important for most kinds of renewable energy sources?

_____

_____

_____

_____

Making Connections

4. Rate the four renewable energy sources from this section from best to worst. Decide on the criteria you will use to determine which is best and which is worst. Explain your reasoning.

_____

_____

_____

_____

_____

5. Rate the three nonrenewable energy sources from this section from best to worst. Decide on the criteria you will use to determine which is best and which is worst. Explain your reasoning.

_____

_____

_____

_____

Exploring

6. Research using the Internet and other resources to assess the different methods of producing electricity using renewable energy resources. What methods seem to be favoured? Why? (See **Figure 3** on page 173 of your textbook.)

_____

_____

_____

_____

_____

_____

Reflecting

7. How do you think the electrical energy needs of your area might be met 50 years from now?

_____

_____

_____

Describe how solar cells be combined with other energy sources.

_____

_____

_____

_____

_____

_____

_____

How many people in North America are using solar cells in their homes?

_____

_____

_____

_____

How I Am Being Assessed _____
_____

Fossil Fuels or Nuclear Power?

What Do You Think?

In your group, discuss the statement and the points for and against. Write down any additional points that your group considers.

Statement	
Future electricity needs should be met using additional nuclear generating stations rather than fossil fuel stations.	
For	**Against**
• Nuclear energy can supply a great deal of electrical energy using only a few generating stations. This is good for the environment.	• Nuclear energy produces dangerous nuclear waste, and currently we do not have a safe way to dispose of it.
• The nuclear industry in Canada is good for the economy. It has created more than 30 000 jobs for people across the country.	• An explosion involving radioactive nuclear material would have a disastrous impact on the environment and the communities around the station.

Search for additional information using the library, CD-ROMs, or the Internet. Prepare a summary of additional information on the topic, and use this information to form your own opinion on the statement.

_____

_____

_____

_____

_____

_____

_____

_____

Share the information with your group members, and then decide whether your group agrees or disagrees with the statement. Write a summary of your group's final position. Prepare to defend your group's position in a class discussion.

_____

_____

_____

_____

_____

_____

_____

_____

_____

How I Am Being Assessed

Understanding Concepts

1. Why are most renewable energy sources not considered a possible solution to our future electrical energy needs?

Exploring

2. Places such as New Zealand use geothermal energy to generate electricity. Geothermal energy is the heat energy taken from beneath the Earth's surface. Is this an option for Canadians? Why or why not? Use Internet or library resources to find out.

Work the Web

How many years do we have left until our nonrenewable energy sources run out?

3.20 Activity

Building a Home Wiring Model

How I Am Being Assessed _____

_____

In this activity, you will build a wiring model of your home. For your model, you will create a floor plan outlining the main electrical devices used in your home, draw a circuit diagram based on your floor plan, and build your model using available materials.

(a) Sketch the living area and label the main electrical loads that are present in each room. A sample drawing of a kitchen is found in **Figure 2** on page 176 of your textbook.

(b) Draw a circuit diagram using cells as the energy source. Outline the devices used in the circuit diagram. **Figure 3** on page 176 of your textbook is a circuit diagram that matches the kitchen in **Figure 2** on the same page.

(d) How do you think you could test your model to make sure it is wired in parallel?

_____

_____

_____

_____

6. Summarize the home wiring model activity in a presentation to the class.

Notes for Presentation

_____

_____

_____

_____

_____

_____

_____

_____

_____

_____

_____

_____

3.20 Activity
Building a Home Wiring Model

How I Am Being Assessed _____

_____

Making Connections

1. Why would an electrician require a circuit diagram? What other jobs might benefit from having a circuit diagram?

   _____

   _____

   _____

   _____

2. Summarize the main points to remember when wiring an electric circuit in parallel.

   _____

   _____

   _____

   _____

   _____

3. List three things that an electrical inspector would check if this were a real home.

   _____

   _____

   _____

   _____

   _____

How I Am Being Assessed _____

_____

Revisit your answers to the What Do You Already Know? questions, page 200, in Getting Started.

Have any of your answers changed?

_____

_____

_____

_____

_____

What new questions do you have?

_____

_____

_____

_____

_____

_____

_____

_____

_____

_____

How I Am Being Assessed _____

_____

Use the concept map to review the major concepts in Unit 3. This map can help you begin to organize the information that you have studied. You can copy the map and then add more links. You can also add more information in each box.

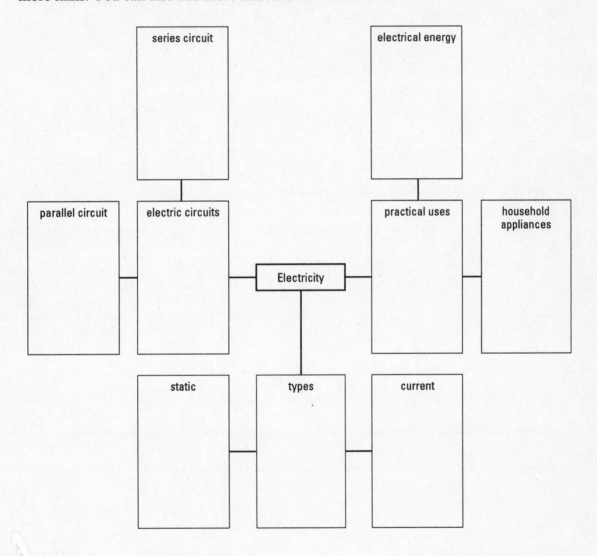

You can use a concept map to review a large topic on a general level, or you can use it to examine a very specific topic in detail. Select one concept from this unit that you need to study in detail and make a detailed concept map for it in the space below.

Challenge

Once you have chosen your Challenge, use the space provided on the following pages to answer the Challenge questions from your text. You may also want to use these pages to record any ideas, or to draw tables, graphs, or sketches that relate to your Challenge.

Challenge	Section and page in textbook
1 Design and Test an Electric Circuit	Section 3.5, page 141 Section 3.6, page 143 Section 3.7, page 145 Section 3.9, page 149 Section 3.10, page 153 Section 3.11, page 156 Section 3.12, page 157 Section 3.13, page 161 Section 3.14, page 163 Section 3.16, page 167
2 Electrical Safety Pamphlet	Section 3.1, page 129 Section 3.2, page 131 Section 3.4, page 137 Section 3.7, page 145 Section 3.10, page 153 Section 3.13, page 161 Section 3.14, page 163 Section 3.15, page 165 Section 3.20, page 177
3 Electric Game Show	Section 3.1, page 129 Section 3.2, page 131 Section 3.3, page 133 Section 3.4, page 137 Section 3.8, page 147 Section 3.10, page 153 Section 3.11, page 156 Section 3.13, page 161 Section 3.14, page 163 Section 3.15, page 165 Section 3.16, page 167 Section 3.18, page 173 Section 3.19, page 175

Challenge Journal

_____

_____

_____

_____

_____

_____

_____

_____

_____

_____

_____

_____

_____

_____

_____

_____

_____

_____

_____

_____

_____

Challenge

Space—What Is Next?

As you learn about space, think about the challenges that scientists have overcome. In all cases, the key is communication. You will be able to show your learning by completing one of the following Challenges.

 1 A Tour Book

The universe is huge with no simple road map available. You have been hired to create a tour book of the universe. You must include directions to all locations and interesting information about the tour site. Your teacher will let you know how many sites must be included in your tour book.

2 A Space Colony

One goal of the space program is to discover a planet that will support human life. This requires water and oxygen at the very least. Design a space colony suitable for humans to occupy permanently.

3 A Space Technology Information Package

You will organize information about space exploration and the study of astronomy, highlighting its influence on our lives, and communicate it effectively to the public.

Select a Challenge. Use pages 378 to 380 to answer the Challenge questions from your textbook and to record your ideas for your challenge.

How I Am Being Assessed _____

_____

1. List five things that are necessary for survival. Begin your list with warmth.

   warmth, _____

2. When people are camping, or when there is a blackout, certain items make life easier, such as matches and candles. List four other items you can use without electricity.

   _____

3. Everyone needs a private area: Think about what things truly make you feel at home. List four of these items.

   _____

   _____

   _____

   _____

   _____

Unit 4 Getting Started

Try This
Activity

How I Am Being Assessed _____

_____

A Packing List

(a) Think about a typical day in your life here on Earth. List five things you do and what you need to do them.

_____

_____

_____

_____

_____

_____

_____

_____

_____

_____

_____

_____

_____

_____

(b) From your list in (a), choose two items that you could live without for three months in space. Cross them out.

(c) What would you need in space that you would not need on Earth? Add three items to your list in (a).

(d) Since you will be in space for three months, how much of each item in (a) will you need? Add the quantities to your list.

(e) Compare your list with those of your classmates. Make changes to your list in (a) if you want to.

4.1 What Can We See in the Sky?

Extension Activity

You probably know more about space than you think you do. For example, you know about the planets in our solar system and you probably know about developments in space technology, like satellites and the Canadarm.

Activity

1. With a partner, answer the following questions.

   (a) What is a shooting star? _____

   (b) What is the Moon made of? _____

   (c) When was the last time astronauts visited the Moon? _____

   (d) Name two planets you can see from Earth. _____

   (e) What is the name of our galaxy? _____

   (f) How big is the universe? _____

   (g) What is astronomy? _____

   (h) What is astrology? _____

   (i) What is our closest star? _____

   (j) Have living things been found in outer space? _____

2. As a class, discuss the answers. Adjust your responses, if necessary.

How I Am Being Assessed _____

_____

Looking for Patterns of Stars

The star map below shows the stars we can see during the winter in Canada. The larger dots are the brighter stars. Draw lines between stars that seem to make patterns. The pattern can be anything you see, such as animals, geometric shapes, or cartoon characters.

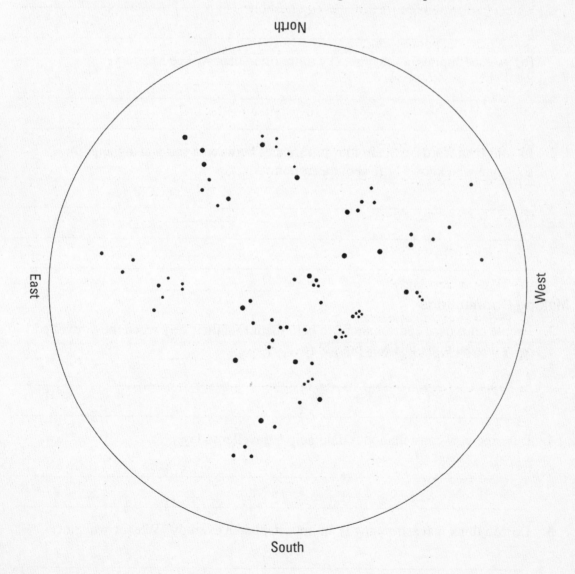

4.1 What Can We See in the Sky?

How I Am Being Assessed _____

_____

Understanding Concepts

1. Give one reason why

   (a) it is very difficult to see Neptune and Pluto without a telescope.

   _____

   _____

   (b) we see Jupiter in the night sky more often than we see Mercury.

   _____

   _____

2. In your own words, explain four differences between a star and a planet for someone who knows little about astronomy.

   _____

   _____

   _____

Making Connections

3. People once used constellations to help them find their way when they travelled. Why do you think this was possible?

   _____

   _____

4. Describe how constellations could help a traveller today.

   _____

   _____

5. Do you think that astronomy is an important area of study? Why or why not?

   _____

   _____

4.2 Planets on the Move

How I Am Being Assessed _____

_____

You Are Earth

(a) You are Earth. Stand east of the model of the Sun and slowly turn counterclockwise. What can you see?

_____

_____

_____

(b) Stand north of the model of the Sun and slowly turn counterclockwise. What can you see?

_____

_____

_____

(c) Stand west of the model of the Sun and slowly turn counterclockwise. What can you see?

_____

_____

_____

(d) Stand south of the model of the Sun and slowly turn counterclockwise. What can you see?

_____

_____

_____

How I Am Being Assessed _____

_____

Understanding Concepts

1. Describe Earth's rotation. What time period does it define for Earth?

    _____

    _____

2. Describe Earth's revolution. What time period does it define for Earth?

    _____

    _____

3. Why does a constellation appear to change position during the night?

    _____

    _____

    _____

4. In **Figure 3** on page 195 of your textbook, the stars appear to revolve around a single spot. What was the camera pointing at?

    _____

    _____

Making Connections

5. (a) Describe two problems that using stars to navigate could cause.

    _____

    _____

    _____

    (b) Would one star be more useful for navigation than any of the others? Explain your answer.

    _____

    _____

4.3 Case Study
Different Views of the Sky
Report

(a) What did each group actually see happening in the sky?

i) the Menomini

_____

_____

ii) the Kwakiutl

_____

_____

iii) the Tsimshian

_____

_____

(b) Why would each of these celestial events have scared people?

_____

_____

_____

(c) Why do you think people were unafraid when a legend explained these events?

_____

_____

_____

(d) What skills did Chinese and Greek astronomers need to make their calendars?

_____

_____

_____

(e) List three ways in which a calendar helped people 3000 years ago.

_____

_____

_____

(f) List three ways in which a calendar helps you today.

_____

_____

_____

(g) Three thousand years ago, Greek and Chinese astronomers mapped 800 stars. We know now that there are billions of stars. Why did these astronomers map only 800 stars?

_____

_____

_____

_____

(h) If the Egyptian statue was in sunlight for only two days of the year, the Sun must be in that position only on those days. How did astronomers from ancient times discover this?

_____

_____

_____

_____

_____

Bonus: Word Scramble

Unscramble the following words:

EEGNDL   _____

DRALACEN   _____

TYMH   _____

TRYMONAOS   _____

RTAS SMPA   _____

4.3 Case Study
Different Views of the Sky
Questions

How I Am Being Assessed _____

_____

Making Connections

1. In Canada, the Sun is highest in the sky at noon on the first day of summer and lowest at noon on the first day of winter. Use this information to design a calendar that will tell you when school begins, when the new year starts, when summer holidays begin, and when it is your birthday, according to the position of the Sun.

2. State two similarities between what people in ancient times used to view the sky and what you use to view it today.

   _____

   _____

3. State two differences between what people used to view the sky in ancient times and what you use to view it today.

   _____

   _____

Exploring

4. The reason we have a day and night cycle is that Earth rotates on its axis once every 24 hours. Create a legend or myth to explain day and night.

_____

_____

_____

_____

_____

_____

_____

_____

_____

_____

Work the Web

Find out more about the myths and legends of different cultures. Summarize your favourite legend or myth.

_____

_____

_____

_____

_____

_____

_____

_____

_____

_____

4.4 Activity
A Seasonal Star Map

How I Am Being Assessed _____

_____

Activity

Constellations change positions during the night. They also seem to change position from one night to the next.

> ✋ You must have the permission and supervision of your parent or guardian to complete these activities.

Part One

(a) Choose a constellation that is visible at this time of year. Make sure it is not too close to the horizon, as that makes viewing difficult.

(b) Make at least three observations, one hour apart.

(c) Make a sketch of your constellation relative to the horizon. Record the direction you are facing.

Table 1: Constellation Motion for One Night   Date: _____

Constellation: _____   Location: _____

Time	Compass direction	Sketch

(d) Given what you know about the rotation of Earth, explain the motion of your constellation over your observation period.

_____

_____

Part Two

(e) Choose a constellation that is visible at this time of year. If possible, chose the same one as you did in **Part One**.

(f) Make five observations, at the same time of night, on five different nights over two or three weeks.

(g) Make a sketch of your constellation, the Moon, and Polaris relative to the horizon. Record the direction you are facing. You may sketch more than one diagram.

Table 1: **Constellation Motion for Many Nights** Time: _____

Constellation: _____   Location: _____

Date	Compass direction	Sketch

(h) Describe the motion of your constellation.

_____

_____

(i) Describe the motion of Polaris. Is this what you expected? Why or why not?

_____

_____

How I Am Being Assessed _____

_____

On December 15 at midnight,

(a) Which constellations would you be able to see near the

northern horizon? _____

western horizon? _____

eastern horizon? _____

southern horizon? _____

(b) Which constellations would you see directly overhead?

_____

(c) After comparing your results from (a) and (b) with another student, do you want to change your predictions? If so, make the changes in a different-coloured pen.

(d) On May 15 at midnight,

Which constellations would you be able to see near the

northern horizon? _____

western horizon? _____

eastern horizon? _____

southern horizon? _____

Which constellations would you see directly overhead?

_____

(e) Set your star map to 8:00 P.M. on December 15 and then to 4:00 A.M. on December 15. Describe what you discovered.

_____

How I Am Being Assessed _____
_____

Understanding Concepts

1. As you rotate the window frame, which constellations can you see no matter what month is shown?

   _____

2. Name the constellations that are visible nearer the horizon at midnight in

   (a) July

   _____

   (b) March

   _____

Making Connections

3. In societies where calendars are not common, the seasonal positions of the constellations are used to indicate when various festivals or activities should take place. If a crop has to be planted in October, what constellations should a North American farmer look for?

   _____

   _____

Exploring

4. Describe how you would try to find a planet in the sky if you were observing it tonight.

   _____

   _____

   _____

   _____

   _____

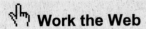

Work the Web

Find out what is visible in your region at night at this time of the year, other than the stars on your star map. Are any planets expected to be visible, or are any comets or meteors predicted to pass through your region?

_____

_____

_____

_____

_____

_____

_____

_____

_____

4.5 The Planets in the Solar System

How I Am Being Assessed _____

_____

Understanding Concepts

1. Create a mnemonic sentence to help you remember, in order, the names of the planets.

Mercury	M	_____
Venus	V	_____
Earth	E	_____
Mars	M	_____
Jupiter	J	_____
Saturn	S	_____
Uranus	U	_____
Neptune	N	_____
Pluto	P	_____

The mnemonic sentence is _____

_____

2. Why are the inner planets also called the terrestrial planets?

_____

_____

3. (a) List two features of Earth that make it unique among the planets.

_____

_____

_____

(b) List two features of Earth that make it similar to the other planets.

_____

_____

Making Connections

4. List five ways that humans have had an impact on Earth. Explain how each way has had positive and negative effects on Earth.

Impact	Positive results	Negative results

Work the Web

Find out more information about your favourite planet. Is there a probe headed there right now? When was the last time a probe reached that planet? Have scientists found out anything new about the planet lately?

_____

_____

_____

_____

_____

_____

_____

4.6 Investigation
Planets and Retrograde Motion
Report

How I Am Being Assessed _____

_____

Analysis and Conclusion

(a) Copy the information from the chalkboard into the space below.

Mars's Motion

0

(b) Fill in **Table 1**.

Table 1 **Mars's Motion**

Date	Distance from "O" (cm)

(c) Use **Table 1** to plot the points on the graph below. Join the points in a smooth curve.

Mars's Motion

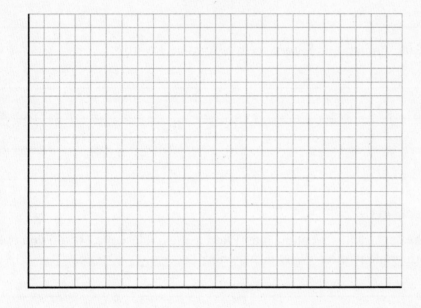

Date

(d) Using your table, when was Mars in retrograde motion? _____

(e) Using your graph, when was Mars in retrograde motion? _____

(f) Was it easier to figure out when Mars was in retrograde using the table or the graph? Why?

_____

_____

4.6 Investigation
Planets and Retrograde Motion

How I Am Being Assessed _____

_____

Understanding Concepts

1. Which planet, Earth or Mars, takes longer to orbit the Sun?

   _____

2. Why do Venus and Mercury never seem to be in retrograde motion?

   _____

   _____

3. Why do Mars, Jupiter, and Saturn seem to loop backward?

   _____

   _____

   _____

   _____

Making Connections

4. If you looked at Uranus, Neptune, and Pluto using a telescope, would you ever see them in retrograde motion? Why or why not?

   _____

   _____

   _____

   _____

   _____

Are any planets currently in retrograde motion? Record your answers.

_____

_____

_____

_____

_____

_____

_____

_____

_____

4.7 Other Objects in the Solar System

Extension Activity

The Moon orbits Earth once every 28 days. Depending on the Moon's position relative to the Sun and Earth, we see different parts, or phases, of the Moon.

Activity

In this activity, you will record your Moon observations in **Table 1**. On as many consecutive nights (or days, depending when the Moon rises) as possible (preferably 28) record the time, relative position, and phase of the Moon.

 To complete this activity, you will need the permission and supervision of your parent or guardian.

Table 1: **The Moon**

Date	Time	Relative position	Phase

Date	Time	Relative position	Phase

(a) What happens to the size of the moon from day to day?

_____

(b) In a month when two full moons occur, the second one is sometimes referred to as a blue moon. What do you think the saying "once in a blue moon" means?

_____

_____

How I Am Being Assessed _____

_____

Debate: Extraterrestrial Mining

"We should learn to manage Earth's resources better, before trying to use extraterrestrial resources."

Record your ideas for or against the above statement. During the panel discussion, fill in the ideas for the opposing point of view.

Support

_____

_____

_____

_____

_____

Oppose

_____

_____

_____

_____

Did you change your opinion after the panel discussion? Why or why not?

_____

_____

_____

_____

4.7 Other Objects in the Solar System

Questions

Understanding Concepts

1. (a) What is an asteroid?

   _____

   _____

   (b) Where is the asteroid belt?

   _____

2. (a) Explain the difference between a meteoroid and a meteorite.

   _____

   _____

   _____

   (b) Why are meteorites less common than meteors?

   _____

   _____

   _____

3. When will Halley's comet be seen next?

   _____

Making Connections

4. Describe what might happen if a giant meteorite crashed into Earth's surface **(a)** on land and **(b)** on water. Use a map to show where such a meteorite would have the least impact on human life.

   _____

   _____

   _____

   _____

Reflecting

5. Space exploration is costly. Do you think that sending probes to explore the minor bodies is necessary? Give two reasons.

_____

_____

_____

_____

_____

Bonus: Word Search

The following words can be found in all directions in the grid.

meteoroid	asteroid belt	minor body	orbit	constellation
astronomy	comet	rotation	revolution	zodiac
legend	myth	satellite	asteroid	meteorite
meteor	planet	star		

Q	E	L	I	H	I	O	N	O	I	T	A	L	L	E	T	S	N	O	C
C	Y	D	O	B	R	O	N	I	M	K	O	H	S	T	U	I	O	B	O
Y	G	O	L	O	R	T	S	A	E	S	T	N	A	I	R	C	I	R	M
M	D	H	Y	N	J	L	M	S	B	Y	I	T	T	R	K	M	T	U	E
O	J	L	M	O	K	E	G	T	M	P	I	J	E	O	B	V	U	C	T
N	J	H	T	I	V	G	N	E	U	B	K	J	L	E	J	I	L	C	R
O	U	I	R	T	E	E	L	R	R	R	O	B	L	T	F	V	O	S	D
R	M	A	U	A	O	N	Z	O	D	I	A	C	I	E	R	O	V	F	D
T	T	S	E	T	C	D	F	I	H	Y	T	G	T	M	E	T	E	O	R
S	H	G	F	O	E	J	M	D	I	O	R	O	E	T	E	M	R	B	D
A	S	T	E	R	O	I	D	B	E	L	T	F	V	T	E	N	A	L	P

How I Am Being Assessed _____

_____

Complete the graphic organizer below to summarize what you can see from Earth.

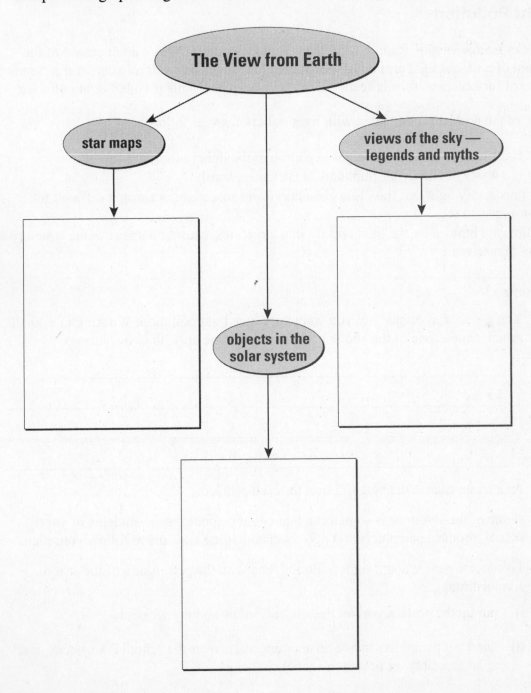

How I Am Being Assessed	_____
	_____

Light Pollution

You can see fewer stars from the city than from the country. Why? It is because of the amount of artificial light around us. Artificial light shines upward, reflects off the clouds and hard surfaces, and then is scattered in the atmosphere. This is called light pollution.

Some of the problems associated with light pollution are as follows:

- It is difficult to observe the night sky through the light pollution.
- It is a waste of energy to illuminate areas unnecessarily.
- Unnecessary light that travels horizontally can cause glare, making it difficult for motorists to see.
- Birds are blinded by the light and fly into structures, causing damage to the structure and to themselves.

Activity

(a) You are an astronomer and you want to reduce light pollution. Working in a small group, choose one of the above problems and come up with two solutions.

  _____

  _____

  _____

  _____

(b) As a class, choose the best solution for each problem.

(c) If one of the solutions is something that could be done by the students of your school, produce pamphlets and posters encouraging students to follow your plan.

(d) To educate people about light pollution, and with the permission of the school administration,

  i)   put up the posters, and let the students know about your plan

  ii) hand out pamphlets, make an announcement over the school PA system, speak at an assembly, or present a school challenge

How I Am Being Assessed _____

_____

(a) Do you think the image on page 211 of your textbook would have been as accurate if a time-lapse photo of 100 h had been taken by a camera attached to a telescope here on Earth? Why or why not?

_____

_____

_____

(b) Why are more instruments added to the HST rather than being sent into orbit on their own?

_____

_____

_____

(c) List two advantages to sending instruments into orbit separate from the HST.

_____

_____

(d) Why wouldn't the telescope naturally stay pointed in the same direction?

_____

_____

_____

(e) How could information from these galaxies help scientists understand more about our galaxy and solar system?

_____

_____

_____

_____

4.8 Case Study
Telescopes

Questions

How I Am Being Assessed _____

_____

Understanding Concepts

1. (a) List two problems that might make it difficult to use telescopes to see the sky from Earth.

    _____

    _____

   (b) Where would you build an observatory to avoid these problems? Explain your choice.

    _____

    _____

2. How does the image in **Figure 4** on page 211 of the textbook allow scientists to "look back in time" ?

    _____

    _____

Making Connections

3. How have improvements in technology changed our view of the universe?

    _____

    _____

🖑 Work the Web

Investigate Canada's role in the development of the Next Generation Space Telescope. Record your information in point form.

_____

_____

_____

_____

How I Am Being Assessed _____

_____

Making Connections

1. What skills and attitudes does an artist need to capture what a camera cannot?

   _____

   _____

   _____

2. If you were going to follow a similar career path, what courses would you take in high school and college or university?

	Courses
High school	
College	
University	

☞ Work the Web

Find out more about the NASA Art Program.

_____

_____

_____

_____

_____

4.10 Case Study
The Sun: An Important Star

How I Am Being Assessed _____

_____

(a) Why is the Sun the most important star? Give two reasons.

_____

_____

(b) Why do we want to learn more about the Sun?

_____

_____

_____

(c) Describe the process of nuclear fusion. Include a diagram.

_____

_____

_____

_____

(d) What might happen to living things on Earth when the Sun runs out of fuel?

_____

_____

(e) When might this happen?

_____

(f) Do some research and explain why everyone does not use solar panels.

_____

_____

_____

(g) Why do we send unpiloted probes to study the Sun?

_____

_____

_____

(h) What is the temperature of the photosphere? the corona? the core?

_____

_____

_____

(i) List two differences between a solar flare and a solar prominence.

_____

_____

_____

(j) Graph the sunspot data from **Table 1** on page 216 of the textbook. Write a title for your graph. Connect the points.

Graph 1: _____

Number of Sunspots

Year

(k) In what years was sunspot activity at a peak? _____

(l) In what years was sunspot activity the least? _____

(m) How many years is one cycle? _____

How I Am Being Assessed _____

_____

The Brightness of Stars

Indicate, by using different colours, how much of the grid is lit up at 10 cm, 20 cm, 30 cm, 40 cm, and 50 cm away from the black paper and cardboard. Fill in the legend.

☐ 10 cm away   ☐ 20 cm away   ☐ 30 cm away   ☐ 40 cm away   ☐ 50 cm away

LEGEND: ☐ 10 cm away   ☐ 20 cm away   ☐ 30 cm away
☐ 40 cm away   ☐ 50 cm away

(a) Move the graph paper cardboard to 20 cm, 30 cm, 40 cm, and 50 cm away from the black paper and cardboard. What happened? Were more or fewer squares lit? Was the light brighter or fainter?

_____

_____

_____

(b) What is the significance of a star's light being quite faint at night?

_____

_____

4.10 Case Study
The Sun: An Important Star

How I Am Being Assessed _____

_____

Understanding Concepts

1. Why is the Sun so bright? Why are other stars so faint?

_____

_____

_____

2. Describe the differences between a solar flare and a solar prominence. Which one affects us and how?

_____

_____

_____

_____

_____

3. Describe the process that occurs in the Sun's core to produce so much energy.

_____

_____

_____

4. When is the next year of maximum sunspot activity predicted to be?

_____

_____

_____

Making Connections

5. Is the possible "death" of the Sun in five billion years a problem that we should be worrying about? Why or why not?

_____

_____

_____

_____

_____

Reflecting

6. Why do we consider the Sun our most important star?

_____

_____

_____

Work the Web

The number of sunspots per year increases and decreases in a regular cycle. Find out where we are in the cycle.

_____

_____

_____

_____

_____

_____

4.11 Galaxies and Star Clusters *Extension Activity*

How I Am Being Assessed _____

_____

Galaxies can be classified into three categories: elliptical, spiral, and irregular. The Milky Way, where we live, is a spiral galaxy. The Sun is found on the outer part of one of the arms.

Activity

Classify each of the following galaxies as either elliptical, spiral, or irregular.

How I Am Being Assessed _____

_____

Model a Spiral Galaxy

Make your own spiral galaxy model.

One way is to use a plastic container, water, a stir stick, and a drop of food colouring. Place the water in the container, add a drop of food colouring, and stir. Make a prediction first.

What will happen?

_____

_____

_____

_____

_____

Observations

_____

_____

_____

_____

Diagram

How I Am Being Assessed _____

_____

Understanding Concepts

1. How are galaxies classified? Draw and label an example of each.

2. Arrange the following in order of size, starting with the largest: star cluster, galaxy, universe, star, planet.

   _____

3. How do you think the Milky Way galaxy got its name?

   _____

   _____

✍ Work the Web

Which galaxy is your favourite? Find out more and summarize the information in a paragraph.

_____

_____

_____

_____

4.12 Investigation
Flame Tests

Report

How I Am Being Assessed _____

_____

Observation

Table 1

Substance	Flame colour
wooden splint	
lithium	
sodium	
potassium	
barium	
copper (II)	
unknown	

Analysis and Conclusion

(a) What was the identity of the unknown substance? How did you decide?

_____

_____

_____

How I Am Being Assessed _____

_____

Understanding Concepts

1. A sample of an unknown white solid is burned. The flame is a deep red. Is the sample table salt (sodium chloride)? Why or why not?

   _____

   _____

   _____

Making Connections

2. How do flame tests relate to the study of the stars?

   _____

   _____

   _____

   _____

Bonus: Crossword Puzzle

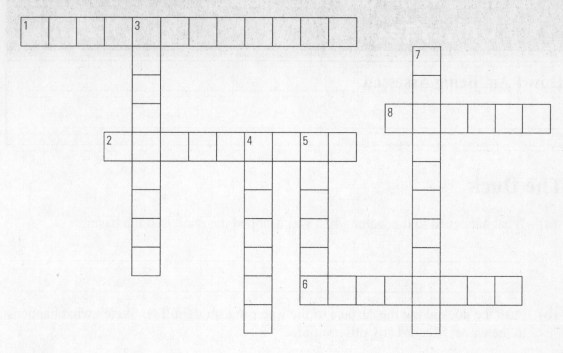

Clues:

1. Instrument used to look at the visible spectrum.
2. The study of outer space.
3. Instrument used to look at distant objects.
4. Planet that is the sister to Uranus.

5. A shooting star.
6. Takes 24 h for Earth to complete.
7. Tests done in this lab.
8. Spiral _____.

How I Am Being Assessed

The Duck

(a) What happened to the water when you dropped the duck into the basin?

_____

_____

(b) Push the duck along the surface of the water in a straight line. Sketch what happens to the waves. Record any observations.

_____

_____

_____

_____

_____

(c) What happened to the wavelength behind the duck?

_____

_____

_____

(d) What happened to the wavelength in front of the duck?

_____

_____

_____

(e) Rewrite the sentence using the correct word:

The wavelength gets shorter as an object moves <u>toward / away from</u> the observer.

The wavelength gets longer as an object moves <u>toward / away from</u> the observer.

How I Am Being Assessed _____

_____

Understanding Concepts

1. Label the ripples that have shorter wavelengths and those that have longer wavelengths. Indicate the direction of movement of the object causing the waves.

2. What does "red shift" mean?

   _____

   _____

   _____

   _____

3. If astronomers were to observe a "blue shift" for a certain star, what could they conclude? Why?

   _____

   _____

   _____

   _____

   _____

4. Sketch a diagram of the ripples that an object travelling from the top to the bottom of this page would make.

Work the Web

Where is the edge of the universe? Can you find any photos of the edge of the universe?

_____

_____

_____

_____

_____

_____

_____

_____

_____

_____

_____

4.14 Activity
A Model of the Expanding Universe

Extension Activity

How I Am Being Assessed _____

_____

Scientists are recording spectroscopic patterns for all elements found on Earth. These patterns tell us what elements are contained in certain compounds.

Activity

After comparing the spectroscopic patterns of the four stars with the spectroscopic patterns of the elements below, list the elements found in the stars.

H
He
Na
Ca
Hg

Star A

Star A contains _____

Star B

Star B contains _____

Star C

Star C contains _____

Star D

Star D contains _____

4.14 Activity
A Model of the Expanding Universe

How I Am Being Assessed _____

_____

Spectroscopy

What did you see?

Describe what you saw when you looked through the spectroscope at the

white light source

_____

_____

potassium permanganate solution placed in front of the white light source

_____

_____

Absorption spectra of
potassium permanganate
solution:

Translucent solution #1: _____

_____

_____

Absorption spectra:

Translucent solution #2: _____

_____

_____

Absorption spectra:

4.14 Activity

A Model of the Expanding Universe

Report

How I Am Being Assessed _____

_____

Observations

Table 1

	Measured Distances (cm)			Calculated Distances (cm)	
	A to B	B to C	C to D	A to C	B to D
orange stage					
basketball stage					

Analysis and Conclusion

6. Look at how much the distances A to B, B to C, and C to D increased when you inflated the balloon to the second stage. Compare those increases.

_____

_____

7. Imagine you are standing on A while the balloon inflates.

(a) Which dot would appear to be moving away from you the most quickly?

_____

(b) Which dot would appear to be moving away from you the most slowly?

_____

(c) Which dot would appear to be moving toward you?

_____

8. Imagine that the dots are galaxies of stars. Complete this sentence by circling the correct word.

"The galaxies that are <u>closer to/ further from</u> Earth seem to be moving away from Earth faster than galaxies that are <u>closer to/ further from</u> us."

Copyright © 2003 Nelson   *4.14 Activity: A Model of the Expanding Universe* **349**

4.14 Activity

A Model of the Expanding Universe

Questions

How I Am Being Assessed _____

_____

Understanding Concepts

1. **(a)** What instrument does an astronomer use to determine the patterns of light of a star or galaxy?

   _____

   (b) What can the patterns of light tell a scientist about a star or galaxy?

   _____

   _____

   (c) Why is using the instrument from (a) better than using only a telescope?

   _____

   _____

Reflecting

2. Although the balloon model was useful to illustrate an expanding universe, it had a major limitation. What was that limitation? (Hint: What about the galaxies that are inside the balloon?)

   _____

   _____

3. Describe a model of the expanding universe that would eliminate the limitation mentioned in question 2. Make a sketch if necessary.

   _____

   _____

   _____

   _____

   _____

Activity

Read the following article and answer the questions below using correct spelling and grammar and full sentences.

RESEARCHERS CREATE A MINI BIG BANG

by Nigel Hawkes, the *Ottawa Citizen*, February 10, 2000

LONDON-Scientists have recreated a state of matter that last existed ten microseconds after the universe began.

By making lead atoms collide into each other at nearly the speed of light, they produced a hot broth in which quarks, the tiniest particles of matter, roamed around freely instead of being bound indissolubly together, as they are in all normal matter.

The discovery, at the CERN laboratory in Geneva, is a huge advance, throwing light both on the origin of the universe and on the nature of matter. It is also a feather in the cap of European science because an American atom smasher was in the hunt and close to making the same discovery.

Physicists, including two teams from Birmingham University, use the Super Proton Synchrotron at CERN to accelerate lead ions to 99.99 per cent of the speed of light (297 600 kilometres per second) and smash them into lead targets. Lead was used because it is so heavy that a lot of energy is released in the collision.

The result was a short-lived fireball reaching temperatures of a million million degrees Celsius, 100 000 times as hot as the centre of the Sun.

The "Little Bang" experiments reproduce conditions that existed immediately after the Big Bang, when temperatures were immensely high and energy [was] very concentrated.

Theory indicates that under these conditions, quarks and gluons (the massless particles that normally hold quarks together) could have existed freely, in a form known as a quark-gluon plasma. Within a fraction of a second, however, they would have condensed into everyday particles such as protons and neutrons, rather like steam condensing into droplets of water, as the universe expanded and cooled.

(Continued)

Seven experiments at CERN were set up to observe the effects of the collisions. "The fireball exists for only the tiniest fraction of a second," said David Evans of the University of Birmingham. "We have to work out what happens by studying the particles that escape from the fireball."

No single experiment on its own can probe that the quark-gluon plasma was created, but all seven taken together are, Dr Evans says, "very compelling." A seminar was held yesterday at CERN to report the findings.

Professor Luciano Maiani, Director-General of CERN, said: "This result is an important step forward in the understanding of the early evolution of the universe."

Yesterday's results are another step in a long march that began with the Greek concept of matter as consisting of atoms, particles that could not be split. The twentieth century showed that they were divisible, and a growing menagerie of sub-atomic particles emerged.

The ruling theory of physics, called the Standard Model, holds that all these particles are made up of yet more fundamental particles called quarks, held together by gluons. But until now, no machine on Earth had been able to isolate a quark

Questions

1. What did scientists do? (Paragraph 2)

   _____

   _____

   _____

   _____

   _____

2. Why was lead used? (Paragraph 4)

   _____

   _____

   _____

   _____

3. What was the result? (Paragraph 5)

   _____

   _____

   _____

4. What did Luciano Maiani say? (Paragraph 10)

_____

_____

_____

_____

_____

5. What is the ruling theory of physics? What does it state? (Paragraph 12)

_____

_____

_____

_____

_____

_____

_____

_____

_____

How I Am Being Assessed _____

_____

Stirring Things Up

1. Use a stick to stir a bucket of water and sand. What happens to the sand? Draw a diagram.

    _____

    _____

    _____

    _____

    _____

2. What happens if you try to stir the water the opposite way? Draw a diagram.

    _____

    _____

    _____

    _____

    _____

3. How does this model support the theory of the origin of the solar system?

    _____

    _____

    _____

How I Am Being Assessed _____

_____

Understanding Concepts

1. What is the estimated age of the universe?

   _____

2. How does the Big Bang Theory explain an expanding universe?

   _____

   _____

3. How could you use all the students in your class to model the expanding universe?

   _____

   _____

   _____

   _____

4. What force is responsible for bringing together particles in space?

   _____

5. How is the formation of a star linked to the formation of the solar system?

   _____

   _____

Reflecting

6. How does a scientific theory, such as the Big Bang Theory, differ from a belief?

   _____

   _____

   _____

   _____

Work the Web

People in all parts of the world have had, and still have, other ideas about the origin of the universe. Find out about two of those ideas.

_____

_____

_____

_____

_____

_____

How I Am Being Assessed _____

_____

Complete the graphic organizer below to summarize, in point form, what you have learned about space.

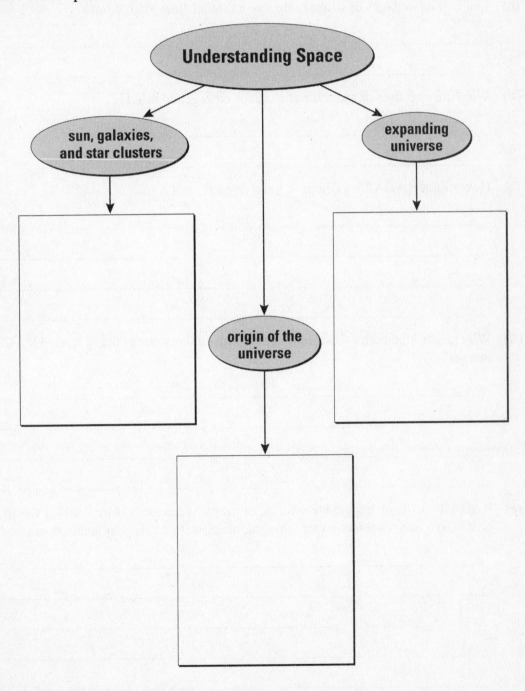

> **How I Am Being Assessed** _____
>
> _____

(a) List two advantages of using radio waves rather than visible light.

_____

_____

(b) What are two uses of radar other than for emergency relief?

_____

_____

(c) How might RADARSAT help in your region?

_____

_____

_____

_____

(d) Why might it be better to search for underground resources using RADARSAT images?

_____

_____

_____

_____

(e) RADARSAT is an expensive system, but it provides great benefits. Is it worth the cost? Give two reasons why or why not, along with a brief explanation of each.

_____

_____

_____

_____

_____

4.16 Case Study Satellites

How I Am Being Assessed _____

_____

Tracking Satellites

You will need Internet access and a star map or planisphere. Binoculars are optional.

On your star map,

1. Research which satellites will be passing over your region in the next few weeks. Interpret the information to determine the satellites' paths.

2. Trace and label the paths of two of the satellites.

3. Choose a clear night and a time to view the night sky.

 Obtain your parent's or guardian's permission and supervision to go out at night to make these observations. Dress appropriately for the weather.

4. Try to observe the satellites you have researched. Using binoculars may help.

Date: _____

Time: _____

Satellite name: _____

Did you see the satellite? Why or why not?

_____

_____

Date: _____

Time: _____

Satellite name: _____

Did you see the satellite? Why or why not?

_____

_____

_____

How I Am Being Assessed _____

_____

Understanding Concepts

1. List five uses for satellites.

   _____

   _____

   _____

2. What are two benefits of using RADARSAT in Canada?

   _____

   _____

Making Connections

3. Radar is related to bats. Explain how.

   _____

   _____

   _____

   _____

   _____

4. Who should be responsible for cleaning up the pieces of space junk that crash to Earth? Give reasons for your answer. (Remember that some of these falling pieces contain nuclear waste.)

   _____

   _____

   _____

   _____

   _____

Find out more about the satellites orbiting Earth. Record your information in point form.

_____

_____

_____

_____

_____

_____

_____

_____

4.17 The International Space Station

Try This Activity

How I Am Being Assessed _____

_____

Manual Skill

While working outside the ISS, astronauts must wear bulky space suits. At the same time, they must perform delicate procedures with extremely sensitive equipment. To get an idea of how difficult this is, try the following tasks while wearing bulky or heavy gloves: tighten a nut on a bolt, operate a VCR, use tweezers to pick up a feather.

How did it go? Describe any problems you had. Were you able to solve them? How?

Tighten a nut on a bolt

_____

_____

_____

_____

Operate a VCR

_____

_____

_____

_____

Use tweezers to pick up a feather

_____

_____

_____

_____

How I Am Being Assessed _____

_____

Understanding Concepts

1. List five uses of a space station.

_____

_____

_____

2. What is Canada's role in the construction of the ISS?

_____

_____

_____

Making Connections

3. How does living on the ISS relate to starting a space colony?

_____

_____

_____

Work the Web

The Canadarm is Canada's major contribution to the ISS. Find out more about the Canadarm and summarize your findings.

_____

_____

_____

_____

_____

How I Am Being Assessed _____

_____

Your Sense of Balance

Here are two activities you can do to test your sense of balance.

> ✋ Have spotters nearby in case you lose your balance.

1. Stand on one leg with your eyes open. Close both eyes and try to maintain your balance. Describe what happened.

    _____

    _____

    _____

2. Stand on one leg facing a striped sheet or blanket held by two students. Try to maintain your balance as the blanket is moved sideways, as shown in **Figure 5** on page 234 of your text. Describe what happened.

    _____

    _____

    _____

Bonus: Word Scramble

Unscramble the following words.

RMI   _____

NIOAAINRTLNTE EPACS TTAIOSN   _____

VTRIAGY   _____

SOTANRUAT   _____

ITRNIAODA   _____

NCBLEAA   _____

ERHRACSE   _____

How I Am Being Assessed _____

_____

Understanding Concepts

1. In your own words, describe why astronauts appear to be floating in the ISS, even though gravity is pulling on them.

    _____

    _____

    _____

2. Describe two effects of constant free fall on the human body. Why do these effects occur?

    _____

    _____

    _____

3. Astronauts must spend a long time exercising each day. Why?

    _____

    _____

    _____

Making Connections

4. Choose one of the health problems described. How does the research related to it affect the lives of people not involved in space flight?

    _____

    _____

    _____

What sorts of health problems do the cosmonauts and astronauts aboard the ISS have to watch for? How do they stay healthy? Record your answers in point form.

_____

_____

_____

_____

_____

_____

_____

_____

_____

Spinoffs of the Space Program

How I Am Being Assessed _____

_____

1. Choose a recently developed product and research how it began with the space program. Use the library or the Internet to help you research.

Product: _____

What was this product developed for in space?	
How does this product benefit Earth?	
Should this product continue to be developed? (Give at least two reasons.)	

2. Design a poster that includes the following:

   - a title
   - an image or drawing of the product or one of its applications
   - a clear explanation of what it was developed for in space
   - the benefits of the product on Earth
   - your opinion as to whether you think this product should continue to be developed (two reasons)

Use colour, sketches, photos, and computer applications as appropriate. Use proper sentences, and check your spelling and grammar.

Use this space to create your poster.

4.19 Activity

Spinoffs of the Space Program

How I Am Being Assessed _____

_____

Understanding Concepts

1. What is meant by the term "spinoff"?

   _____

   _____

2. Which spinoffs from **Table 1** on page 237 of your textbook do you think are likely linked to Canada's contributions to the space program?

   _____

   _____

   _____

   _____

Making Connections

3. List four space spinoffs that are now part of your daily life.

   _____

   _____

Work the Web

Find out more about the links between products developed for space and their use on Earth. Add the information to your poster.

_____

_____

_____

_____

How I Am Being Assessed _____

_____

Design an Alien

One day, while you are out for a walk, you find a new life form—an alien. No one believes you, so you have to build a model and write a summary of what you observed about the alien.

You must include

- a model or picture of the alien
- labels on your picture or model for at least 15 features of the alien (such as size, shape, limbs, body covering)
- a description of where the alien came from and how
- your thoughts about whether the alien was having trouble surviving here on Earth and why
- an explanation of why the alien is on Earth

Display your alien to the class.

How I Am Being Assessed _____

_____

Space Exploration

People in favour of space exploration give many good reasons why it will benefit the human race. People against space exploration feel strongly that the disadvantages outweigh the benefits.

Activity

Choose your position: **For** or **Against** space exploration.

Brainstorm a list of six reasons that support your point of view. Think about economics, ethics, environmental issues, politics, and available technology.

_____

_____

_____

_____

_____

_____

_____

Create a poster that outlines your six reasons. Pictures can be included.

4.20 Explore an Issue
Our Future in Space

Questions

How I Am Being Assessed _____

_____

Making Connections

1. List five ways that space exploration and research have helped people.

   _____

   _____

   _____

2. Do you think that we should be spending time and money exploring space? Why or why not? Give two reasons.

   _____

   _____

   _____

   _____

   _____

Work the Web

What are our plans for space? Summarize your answer in two or three paragraphs.

_____

_____

_____

_____

_____

_____

_____

_____

Unit 4 Summary

What Have You Learned?

How I Am Being Assessed _____

_____

Revisit your answers to the What Do You Already Know? questions, page 300, in Getting Started.

Have any of your answers changed?

_____

_____

_____

_____

_____

What new questions do you have?

_____

_____

_____

_____

_____

_____

_____

_____

_____

_____

How I Am Being Assessed _____

_____

Use the concept map to review the major concepts in Unit 4. This map can help you organize the information that you have learned. You can add more links to your map. You can also add more information in each box.

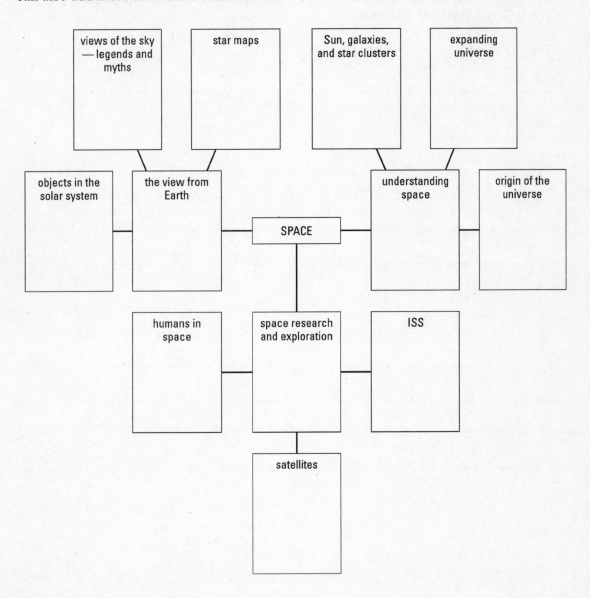

You can use a concept map to review a large topic on a general level, or you can use it to examine a very specific topic in detail. Select one concept from this unit that you need to study in detail, and make a detailed concept map for it in the space below.

Challenge

Once you have chosen your Challenge, use the following pages to answer the Challenge questions from your text. Use these pages to record your ideas, or to draw tables, graphs, or sketches that relate to your Challenge.

Challenge	Section and page in textbook	
1 A Tour Book	Section 4.1, page 193 Section 4.2, page 195 Section 4.5, page 203 Section 4.7, page 209 Section 4.10, page 216 Section 4.11, page 219 Section 4.13, page 223 Section 4.15, page 227 Section 4.17, page 231 Section 4.18, page 235	
2 A Space Colony	Getting Started, page 191 Section 4.2, page 195 Section 4.4, page 199 Section 4.5, page 203 Section 4.8, page 212 Section 4.9, page 213 Section 4.10, page 216 Section 4.11, page 219 Section 4.14, page 225	Section 4.18, page 235 Section 4.20, page 239
3 A Space Technology Information Package	Section 4.3, page 197 Section 4.5, page 203 Section 4.6, page 205 Section 4.7, page 209 Section 4.8, page 212 Section 4.10, page 216 Section 4.12, page 221 Section 4.13, page 223 Section 4.15, page 227 Section 4.16, page 229 Section 4.17, page 231	Section 4.18, page 235 Section 4.19, page 237

_____

_____

_____

_____

_____

_____

_____

_____

_____

_____

_____

_____

_____

_____

_____

_____

_____

_____

_____

_____

_____

_____

_____